CW00405429

Quit Smoking Easy:
Guided Self-Hypnosis& Meditations To Stop Smoking Addiction& Smoking Cessation Including Positive Affirmations, Visualizations & Relaxation Techniques

By Meditation Made Effortless

Table of Contents

Introduction 1

Induction 3

Deepener 6

Be a Non-Smoker Script 8

Deep Relaxation Script 13

Inner Child Healing 17

Increased Self Confidence 21

Light the Fire Within – Empowering Yourself 25

Quit Smoking Confidence 32

Stop Smoking Script 36

Smoking Pros and Cons 41

Road to Stopping Smoking 45

Keep the Motivation Going 52

Smoking Cessation 56

Appreciate Yourself 61

Sleep Better 65

Stop smoking II 70

White Light Meditation 84

Sleep Reprogramming 90

Stop Smoking with Self Hypnosis 96

The Time Distortion Method 103

Learning to Relax 109

Smoking Cessation II 119

Hypnosis Benefits Script 124

Silky Breathing 130

Staying Committed Script.................................. 136

Get rid of the Compulsion Script 143

Live a Smoke Free Life 149

Affirmations 153

To the Narrator

The Introduction, Induction, and Deepener should be 45 Min Long
Be a Non Smoker should be 15 Min Long
Deep Relaxation should be 20 Min Long
Inner Child Healing should be 15 Min Long
Increased Self Confidence should be 20 min long
Light the Fire Within should be 20 min long
Quit Smoking Confidence should be 20 min long
Stop Smoking I should be 15 min long
Smoking Pros and Cons should be 25 min long
Road to Stop Smoking should be 20 min long
Keep the Motivation Going should be 20 min long
Smoking Cessation I should be 20 min long
Appreciate Yourself should be 20min long
Stop Smoking II should be 20 min long
Sleep Reprogramming should be 40 min long
White Light Meditation should be 20 min long
Stop Smoking with Self Hypnosis should be 22 min long
The Time Distortion should be 25 min long
Learning to Relax should be 40 min long
Sleep Better should be 15 min long
Smoking Cessation II should be 15 min long

Hypnosis Benefits should be 25 min long
Silky Breathing should be 25 min long
Staying Committed should be 25min long
Get Rid of The Compulsion should be 35
min long
Suggestions should be 35min long

"…" means take a breath while speaking before you continue.

PAUSE (for a few breaths)

LONGER PAUSE (give time to allow the listener time to imagine what you've suggested)

Introduction

Thank you for choosing **Quit Smoking Hypnosis audio**…And choosing this audio only means, you have taken a step towards loving yourself even more. In the past, you have smoked innumerable cigarettes and seen the consequences of smoking on your body. It may have given you temporary pleasure every time you smoked one, but eventually it kills by damaging your lungs, mouth, and throat. It may have caused you feel guilty of knowing

Quitting smoking is one of the best decisions you can make to live a healthier and happier life. And, it is never too late to quit. When you quit smoking, you increase your life expectancy, reduce the risk of lung cancer, high blood pressure, renal diseases, and sexual dysfunction. It also reduces the risk of respiratory complications.

The coughing will be reduced to quite an extent and you will have high levels of energy with better ability to taste food. The sense of smell and taste will improve significantly. Some of the other benefits of quitting smoking include better skin and improved complexion. The financial benefits are of course that you will save money.

This audio recording will not only reinforce the decision of quitting smoking but also reprogram your mind to relax your mind, body, and sleep better. This will help you manage your stress better and will eliminate the craving of picking up a cigarette significantly.

Pause

So, congratulations on taking this step of quitting smoking and making a wonderful decision to better health.

Pause

I would like you to sit or lay comfortably, where you will not be distracted. Do not listen to this audio when your mind requires your conscious attention.

Pause

Listen to this audio only when you are relaxed and stationary. Please use headphones so that you can focus on the sound of my voice.

Let us start…

Begin recording

Induction

You are now listening to the sound of my voice… and the sound of my voice only …and as you continue to listen to each word I say…you allow yourself to relax more and more.

Pause

I wonder if you could take a deep breath…hold it for a count of 5… and then exhale.

Pause

Let's start now.

Breathe in Deeply…

Pause

Hold for a count of 5

1… 2…3…4…and 5

Now, exhale…
Pause

Once more, take another deep breath…

Breathe in…

Hold for a count of 5 — 1, 2, 3, 4, 5 (slowly)

Now, breathe out…
Pause

Once more, take another deep breath —

Breathe in

Hold for a count of 5 — 1, 2, 3, 4, 5 (slowly)

Now, breathe out

Pause

And, come back to your normal breathing pattern…

Pause

— And, I wonder… if you could simply bring all your focus and attention to the centre of your eye-brows...with your eyes closed…try to look at the centre of your brows and focus on the point between them…that's right.

Pause

In a moment, I am going to talk to that part of you, which is highly creative…the part that knows exactly how to help you imagine or create anything with the help of your mind's eye.

Pause

And… I know you can do it… because everybody can…we all have a creative mind, that has the ability and capability to create and imagine images in our mind.

I know you must have imagined or visualized or day-dreamed many times in your life. And… our creative part helps us imagine and visualize. Isn't it?

With the help of our creative mind, we can visualize, imagine, write, paint, and dream…and I am going to be talking to that part of you today.

Pause

Deepener

Imagine yourself standing on top of a 10 steps staircase and the staircase looks beautiful . As you look at it, you notice its handrails and steps. The staircase leads you to a hallway…and perhaps it is made of stone, wood, or metal, I don't know…but you know. Whatever material it is made of, just get the knowing of it. Feel the handrails with your hands.

You have the capability to imagine yourself standing on top of it…

And, as I count down from 10 down to 0…you notice yourself going down the staircase, starting with your right foot. And, as you go down, you will find yourself becoming twice as relaxed and twice as deep.

Keep your right foot on the top step…

10…let your body relax and feel or imagine yourself going into a beautiful state of relaxation
9…relaxing more and more, going deeper and deeper into the relaxing state of mind
8… getting comfortable and calmer
7…going deeper
6…even deeper and even more relaxed
5…half-way there

4...relaxing more and more with each step down
3...almost there and you can notice the door at the end of the hallway clearly
2...getting to the hallway in a moment...
1...deeply relaxed
0... you are at the bottom of the staircase.

Longer Pause

Be a Non-Smoker Script

And as you stand at the bottom of the staircase, you notice the walls and floor of the hallway and wonder what is behind the door.

You are going to move towards the door with every breath you take and with every word I say…

Pause

You are at the door and as you notice yourself at the door, you touch the door and feel its texture. Perhaps it's rough or smooth…and you notice its color and the door-knob or a handle.

You can listen to the sound of the birds and the wind blowing behind the door…

And, you know that there is a garden behind the door…and you can't wait to open it and explore it.

You are excited to push open the door and explore what lies behind.

Pause

So, slowly…you put your hand on the door knob or handle and push open it…and as you open it, you feel the fresh air on your face and smell the lovely fragrances coming from the flowers. The trees are tall and the grass is green...perhaps moist...

You look around and notice birds chirping and hopping from one branch to another and the trees sway with the wind. The wind caresses you gently as you look around and enjoy the beautiful surroundings.

In the center of the garden, you notice, a small cottage that looks beautiful from outside. The small staircase leading to its patio looks a bit worn out, but you are intrigued and want to look at it from inside.

Pause

The cottage attracts you and you excitingly open the door and reach the room that looks ashy and dark. It has a foul smell that you can barely stand and the walls look tarnished. The inside is completely opposite to the outside...the outside looks beautiful and polished while the inside looks quite raw and ugly...

You also notice the couch and the rug that look quite old. The upholstery of the ottomans and couches are all faded and have lost their sheen and glow.

Pause

It is almost impossible for you to stay indoors and you feel like going out in the beautiful garden to catch a fresh breath of air…

However, you feel a connect with this cottage and feel that it needs cleaning. For that, you magically get everything in the room to clean and refurbish it…because with the creative and powerful subconscious mind, you can create and imagine anything now.

Longer Pause

To make it look beautiful and clean from inside, you need to paint the walls, clean the floor, wash the rug, change the upholstery of the couches and ottoman…

And you have all the power to create a box of tools and everything you need to be able to do all this.

In a moment, you notice… a big box with paints, paint brushes, paint rollers, a ladder, vacuum cleaner, wipers, scrubbers, and many more tools to help you with painting and cleaning.

Pause

I give you a few moments to use your creativity to clean, clear, and make the room look absolutely new and beautiful.

Longer Pause (15 seconds pause)

Everything is neat and clean, the room smells fresh, the walls look beautiful, the floor looks clean…

The furniture has a new upholstery…perhaps its modern or traditional…but it's all new.
And, this makes you stay in here…and relax… as you continue to listen to me…

Pause

You believe that this is your cottage and you belong here…and to be able to stay here, the space needs to be clean and fresh…always.

Perhaps it now looks incredibly beautiful…organized and clean.

Pause

You know now that to be able to even stand in a place, it needs to be clean and fresh. It needs to look nice and should give you a feeling of warmth.

With all that you have changed in here, you not only can stand, but can stay and relax for as long as you want…

And this only means that you would want to keep it this way forever…clean and organized…smelling nice and fresh….no more shady, dark, dull, and smoky…

Deep Relaxation Script

As you continue to listen to me, you drift further and further into a beautiful state of relaxation. Continue to focus on the sound of my voice and the sound of my voice only.

Take a deep breath and let it out slowly.

That's right. Let's take another deep breath. Inhale ....and exhale.

And begin to let any tension from the body move away from you...as you continue to breathe normally and continue to listen to each word I say.

Continue to go further deep into this incredible state of relaxation. Imagine tightening your first very hard as if all the muscles are tensed up....and in a moment, simply loosen up and let go...

Pause

Let's do it with the other hand...tighten your fist and loosen it. Let both the hands go loose and limp. Let them go really relaxed and limp as if they cannot be relaxed any further.

And, now take all your attention to your eyelids, squeeze them hard and after a few seconds, simply let them be relaxed. Let go loose and relaxed…

I wonder if you can send a wave of relaxation to all your body parts starting from your head to the calves of your legs to the soles of your feet. Let your whole body go limp and loosen every part of your body...like a rag doll.

Pause

And the second wave of relaxation from top to bottom that makes you relaxed even more. Allow each muscle to be fully relaxed and you continue to listen to me and feel deeply relaxed.

Now allow your feet to completely become relaxed. And let your soles, ankles, and heels get beautifully relaxed.

Now, send the third wave, as they say that it's more like a charm. So, send the wave through the body from top to toe and see the muscles getting deeply relaxed.

Pause

And this relaxation begins to move up in to the calves of your legs, thighs, and hips. Let all the muscles in your lower body get completely relaxed. In reality, there is no stop to the amount of relaxation you can experience.

Now, let this beautiful feeling of relaxation move up in your torso, chest, and shoulders. Feel the relaxation moving into your upper back, middle back, and lower back…

It continues to move up again to the shoulders, neck, back of your neck, and to your face, relaxing every muscle, nerve, and fibre in your face.

You can easily feel the wave of relaxation in your face, your forehead, the top of your head…making every part in your eyes, eye lids, forehead go absolutely relaxed.

Pause

There is no limit to the relaxation you can experience. And, as I count down from 3 down to 1, with each count down, you will allow yourself to go even deeper with every count down.

Starting at 3…feeling the relaxation everywhere in your body…drifting down and down..

2…becoming even more relaxed…
1….even deeper…

As you continue to listen to the sound of my voice, you are being guided into the relaxation and the deeper you go, the more relaxed you feel, and more relaxed you feel, the deeper you go.

It is just a continuous cycle of deepening relaxation and feeling the feelings of comfort and relaxation. All you can experience right now is the calm and peaceful feelings all inside your body and all over it and as I count again down from 3 down to 1...you can double the relaxation.

Pause

Starting now at 3....double it up
2...going deeper and deeper
1...even more relaxed...

And as the mind relaxes, the mind gets further relaxed. And you can use this relaxation technique anytime you crave a cigarette.

Pause

Remember its all about diverting thoughts of smoking to doing something productive or better and with the help of that, you will be able to relax your mind and relax thoughts about cigarettes.

You would gain better control on your thinking and you will be able to change the action that follow the thoughts.

Inner Child Healing

As you continue to listen to me, you drift further down into this beautiful state of relaxation. You continue to listen to listen to me and that only reinforces the fact that you are serious about non-smoking and living a healthier and positive life.

In a moment, you are going to go back in your past to the first time you picked up a cigarette.

Pause

And, I know you can do it because everybody can. You are going to go back to the time when you picked it up and started to smoke. I am going to count down from 10 down 0 and with each count down, you are going to go deeper into your subconscious mind and reach that time when you first picked it up .

Starting now...at 10, 9, 8.....7......6.....5.....4......3.......2.........1....and 0.

Longer Pause (10 seconds)

You are at the time when you first picked up a cigarette. In your mind, look at the situation....did anyone tell you to try it or you just happened to do it on your own?

Just know the reason and go further back in time when you did not use to smoke at all. The time before the time when you picked it up. The time when you were happy, joyful, and had no stresses of life.

Even younger….that's right.

Longer Pause

Perhaps you are very young…and at school or home. Just look at what's happening around you…and the kinds of clothes you are wearing. Look what you are doing and saying. Notice your younger self closely.

Look at the expressions, the hair, and the skin.

This is your inner child and just imagine if you had a son or daughter like her, would you love her or him? I am sure you did…because as a parent, you would give unconditional love to this child, isn't it?

Pause

Today you are going to meet the child and have a conversation with them about how much you love them. How much you are ready to protect them and guide them in future.

You know that you are much wiser self since you have gone through all the situations that this child will go through. And, you will guide him or her about every future situation and allow them to move through them with all your support, love, and guidance.

You give them some pieces of advice and pearls of wisdom.

And, together you will travel in future when this younger self gets older and is about to pick up his or her first cigarette.

Longer Pause

You both are in the time in future when your past self is about to pick up a cigarette. And, because you have been through this situation and know all the ill effects of smoking. I would like you to speak to your past self about the bad effects of smoking and how it can affect the health.

Know that you have promised your younger self that you will always protect, guide, and take care of them.

So, what would you like to tell your past self as they are about to pick up a cigarette? I want you to have a conversation with him or her and let them know all the effects of it and what you experienced health wise when you smoked cigarettes. Talk to them about how difficult it was to quit and how many times you relapsed.

Longer Pause (10-15 seconds)

And, do not let this past self of yours pick up a cigarette. And, that only means that he or she will remain smoke free for the rest of their life.

The time has come to move forward together and come back to the present time. And, when you are together, you congratulate the past self to listening to you. You appreciate them.

You are a part of your past self and the past self is a part of you....you are both together right now and in a moment, the past self is going to integrate itself into you so that you become whole and complete. You will become one entity that does not smoke and stays healthy for the rest of your life.

Imagine, visualise, or notice, both of you becoming one with each other....imagine the past self is integrating into you and as that happens, you become even more confident, happier, joyful, and strong headed about not smoking. Together as one entity, you are going to live a happier life, a smoke free life, a fulfilling life.

That's right.

Increased Self Confidence

Continue to stay in the deep and focused state of mind, every breath you take allows you to maintain and deepen this miraculous state of mind. Your subconscious mind is infinite and powerful…which can take in all the positive statements and suggestions to help you achieve your goal of sticking to non-smoking and I know you can do that.

Pause

Your wonderful subconscious mind is open to every advantageous idea that I am saying which will bring positive changes to your emotional, mental, and physical well-being.

And with every heart-beat, it gets reinforced into your mind that you are listening to me because you have made a decision to quit smoking. And you continue to listen to me, till the time you are free from it.

Longer Pause

The sound of my voice further relaxes you deeply and helps you to reinforce and strengthen every positive idea said in this recording.

Just continue to float in this beautiful state of mind, let go, and feel calm. Simply enjoying this state, feeling absolutely calm and relaxed.

And, the conscious mind of yours wanders and let it do that...perhaps it goes far away or falls asleep and the inner mind of yours pays attention to me for the ideas that will make your health and life better.

Pause

And this subconscious mind brings out the memory from your childhood where you were absolutely confident, stress free, and secured. Your allow your subconscious to help you find that memory...

Longer Pause

And as you notice that memory from your childhood, you wonder that how can a person this confident and stress free pick up a habit of smoking? This is strange, isn't it?

Longer Pause

Perhaps the self-doubts, fears, or stress made you pick it up to lessen stress or to feel confident, and to think better to clear self-doubts. And, that's what cigarettes do with consequences of affecting your health for life.

Pause

And with this insight today, you are more than happy to let go of fears and self-doubt and living your life with self-confidence is the way to kick any habit that does not do any good to you. And kicking it will allow you to live a joyful and healthy life.

Know that self-doubt and fear are learnt feelings and you can simply unlearn them. What is learnt can be unlearnt because you were not born with it. Isn't it?

Your natural state is to be confident in every situation and with that confidence and assertiveness, you can say **No** to cigarettes.

Pause

The natural state of any person is exactly like a baby. Babies are born free, they laugh, cry, and do many things without any inhibitions. They are absolutely confident.

And you are that kind of a baby…just a grown up one now. And you learnt so many things as a child…learning to walk, ability to walk and get up again after falling, learning to speak, learning to run, you were incredible as a child and you are still.

This was your natural confidence and you would not have done that if you were not confident. Isn't it?

Pause

And no fear, self-doubt, and stress can stop you from achieving what you want to achieve. You are courageous, persistent, confident, and strong.

Your inner mind is full of all the knowledge that you need to know right now. It is the wisest part of you and that part gives you all the guidance about smoking cigarettes.

I am going to be quite for a few moments here so that you have a conversation with the wisest part of you.

Longer Pause (15 seconds pause)

After talking to the wisest part of you, I know you that you are feeling better and you know exactly what you need to do to feel healthy.

From today on, you will be a non-smoker who loves himself or herself fully, completely and deeply. You are someone who wants to enjoy life to the fullest and till the life exists for you. You can live longer without cigarettes and enjoy more gifts of life and gain more experiences.

Light the Fire Within – Empowering Yourself

You continue to relax yourself with every breath you take and go deeper and deeper into your own mind…turning all your awareness inside.

You are reaching the quieter and deeper parts of yourself..

Pause

And you do not have to worry about anyone and anything because the world is taking care of itself without you. All you have to know is that this is your time. The time to be with yourself , to explore yourself, and reach the deepest state of mind.

All your worries, tensions, stresses, thoughts are simply fading away as you focus on the sound of my voice.

You are open to receive all the powerful suggestions that I have to say. There is no need to remember anything, all you have to do is to just listen.

Just let this experience seep into every part of you…that's right.

Pause

And, here and now, you can make possible powerful changes, which are helpful to achieve all that you want to achieve. All that is going to be easy and effortless. When you have made the changes and you come out of this state and go back to the physical world, the changes made here will stay with you.

All these changes regarding your health will stay with you because you want them to stay with you and you want these to be permanent changes.

You can accept that only when you want the changes to stick with you, they stick with you.

Longer Pause

You trust yourself and believe in yourself that you can do it. You can make the changes and you allow them to be with you permanently.

And we will be working together on the changes and you let those changes go deep into your subconscious to make permanent impression in your mind, body, and soul.

As we progress into this, you are beginning to notice that that there will be a change in your behaviour and actions. And these changes will happen everyday for your highest good.

Your brain accepts these changes and you notice new neural pathways being created. And all actions and behaviours regarding the change will only strengthen these neural pathways.

You have the power to change what you want to change. The habit of smoking to habit of drinking water...and you can make all these necessary changes now.

Longer Pause

You can allow a deeper sense of comfort to reach every part of your body and mind. You are unaware of any distractions and you are only focused on each word I say.

You are now deeply relaxed and your mind is beautifully relaxed and open to every word I say to you. You accept these words because these words will allow you to make the necessary changes for you to have a healthy and fulfilling life.

These words have the immense power because you trust these words without any judgement..

Pause

That's right.

You will begin to relax even more and less reactive in situation and to other people. Every day you are becoming calmer and even more relaxed and have more mental clarity. You will stay composed and would be able to think twice before reacting to anyone or any situation.

You acknowledge that you want to remain calm and listening to every word I say only reinforces it. You mental, emotional, and physical wellbeing is enhancing and getting better with every passing day. You are now going to think clearly and focus better. You accept that there is nothing to worry and you are a person with infinite possibilities.

Pause

You do not let any remark from others affect your emotional and mental wellbeing. You love yourself a lot and you won't let it affect by anyone else's negative comments.

They are of no importance to you.

For too long now, you have held yourself back and perhaps the negative thoughts about yourself or the world around you have held you back.

Maybe you have felt too controlled in the past and perhaps that was because of the negative emotions. And, you rise above those negative emotions and feelings and cut the cords with the past now. Your past no longer affects you. And as you do that, you feel free, stronger, and lighter.

Pause

You no longer feel weighed down by all those past negative thoughts and feelings. . You feel much lighter and stronger. You are coming into the light, the beautiful light of peace and calm. You rise above and feel lighter as if you are floating in the air, feeling absolutely relaxed and calm.

And as you notice yourself floating in the air, you notice fluffy clouds all around you. You can feel the softness, fluffiness, and lightness all around you and inside of you. This calm, soft and light feeling reaches every part of your body, in all the places of your being that need to feel calm and relaxed.

Longer Pause

The feeling of lightness is all around you and inside you and you can begin again to build deep sense of appreciation for yourself, strength, confidence, and high self- esteem. You are no longer weighed down by grief or pain. Everything seems so light and you feel free. That's right.

You let all the strength and confidence grow inside of you and you feel it all around you.

You truly accept that you are the person who deserves to be happy and confident. And, it is wonderful to appreciate the changes you have made and want to make for your own good.

Pause

You become aware of all the changes you know are possible and the changes you want to make, related to your health. These are the changes that are right for you. These changes help you accept yourself as happy and strong person.

Pause

You are fully in control and you have taken control of your life and body. With the changes you have made and are willing to make, you have a new sense of being renewed. As that happens, you notice yourself approaching a door that leads you to your future.

Longer Pause

The future that you are creating for yourself, the future that will show you as a changed person for your good.

And the colour of the door is purple and you push open the door, you enter the space of purple colour. All you notice around is purple - mesmerising colour. And you feel so calm and relaxed in this space. Also, feel focused and confident.

This is your future…

And close the door behind you with everything locked behind that does not solve any purpose. That does not do any good to you.

Longer Pause

You have amazing skills and talents that you have been honing for many years. And all this was possible because you believed in yourself. And from beginner to advanced, you changed. You changed your skillset, you got better. All this was possible because of your creative mind and spirit.

Pause

This an extraordinary space to be. You believe in yourself, you love yourself, you love your capabilities, you are confident. You believed that all the changes you made, worked. You have been changing knowingly or unknowingly ever since you came into this world. With the same belief, you can change any habit. You can change your mindset.

And, I know you can quit smoking and you have already done that by listening to me.

Quit Smoking Confidence

And let's imagine that you know all the negative effects of smoking and how it affects your breathing. You may have experienced how smoking has led you to breathe harder, perhaps it has been an effort to breathe.

It may have led to the irritation in the throat and caused you to cough perhaps while with someone at work, or in office meetings or at home...and so much of strain while coughing and the lungs getting grey and smoky air, may have caused quite some damage internally, which is perhaps not visible as yet on the outside.

And, I am sure you know of people who lost their lives to lungs or mouth cancer. Do you know what must have happened to their families?

Longer Pause

Imagine, what will happen to your family and how will you be missed?

Pause

And you are just imagining the future if you continue to smoke the cigarettes. But you can change all this and make it a beautiful future, where you are living a fulfilling and healthy life if you stop cigarettes now.

A beautiful family, work and social life.

You will be breathing clean and fresh air, healing your body fully from inside and looking amazing on the outside.

And all this is possible when you stop smoking NOW.

That's right.

You will live freely with clean and healthy body.

And, you have been a non-smoker already since you last smoked a cigarette. And, the body has started to heal already and you can continue doing that…and continue to heal your body.

Every time you think of a cigarette, you only think of all the bad it has done to your body and what it would continue to do if you choose to continue to smoke.

Pause

By knowing this, you feel a sense of confidence that you can control the urge to smoke and feel great about yourself and your body.

You feel in control. That's right.

And anytime you have an urge to smoke, you will intentionally look at the future in your mind where smoking has done damage to your health so that you know that its right to distract your mind and thoughts to something better.

You can divert your thoughts to drinking water or chewing a gum, or doing something else physically so that you distract your mind completely from smoking to non-smoking.

Pause

And as you divert your mind and thoughts to something else, you notice that with every passing day, your health becomes better and your body blossoms like a garden. And, you decide to take care of your body as your own house.

Pause

You ensure, everything is spick and span, you do not let anything bad come into your house, whether its pests, wild animals, rain water...that you know can damage your house or you. Similarly, you take care of your body just how you take care of your house. Keeping it absolutely neat and clean.

That's right.

Your mind says " No smoking" and you listen to it. You listen to it because your mind is very powerful. It knows what is right for you and what is not. And, the same mind is listening to me because it wants you to quit smoking. Isn't it?

I know you can do it, because everybody can.

Pause

Sometimes, your body may think that it's the boss and would let you pick up a cigarette because it craves it. However, know, that your mind is more powerful than your body and your mind wants you to not smoke and be a non-smoker for the rest of your life.

You want to be healthier, happier, and even more confident…living a happy and fulfilling life.

Longer Pause

You know every time you get a thought of smoking a cigarette, you will divert your mind to do something better and productive. You can choose to drink water, talk to your friends, do household work, or anything else.

That's right.

Stop Smoking Script

Your urge to smoke is not there anymore. HABIT CYCLES, the gorge of your primary complication - that's our concern at present.

Remember!! You are the creator of Habits and you can easily be the destroyer.
To do that, there is a way and that is to make you smoking conscious.

As soon as you get the urge to pick a cigarette, you will be aware of what you're doing.
And if you light it and start to smoke, you will be exceptionally conscious of every single time you indulged in smoking.

Pause

You have become oblivious to smoking, you have been doing it unconsciously. And that's the reason for your perpetuation.

But you are conscious now. The moment you go for that one cigarette, you will think with apprehension.

The moment you get acquainted with your actions, you are no longer a part of the vicious habit cycle.

And now it becomes easy. You know it. You don't want to smoke anymore. With your will power, the path becomes effortless and you know it. There will be no guilt.

Pause

Your consciousness will make you hate smoking. Perhaps you might even stub out the cigarette when you're halfway there. You will hate it.

You wouldn't want to carry on with it. You have got the reason why you smoke and you have made your mind up to put an end to smoking once and for all.

That's it. It's settled. You're done with it. Not tomorrow, not the day after, TODAY! At this very moment, you have already decided to end the habitual cycle. You are not going to smoke any more. No more.

You know the reason why you want to stop. Keep reminiscing about it. The reason is as clear as a crystal in your head.

Pause

Keep reminding yourself of the effects of smoking.

You are quitting because you want to. Without cigarettes there is no coughing, there is no pain, there is no trouble. Without cigarettes there is relaxation, there is rest, there's a feeling of security, happiness towards yourself and your loved ones. You're giving up troubles and gaining what you've always wanted.

Cigarettes is the thing of past

Buying a cigarette will be unnecessary as you don't smoke them anymore. As a result, you will desist to purchase them. Even if you accept a cigarette unknowingly, Straight away you'll be conscious towards it and a sudden impulse will try to restrict you to consume it. Next time, you'll break it into pieces whenever you get hold of it.

Pause

It will make you realize the bad effects it has on you and all the stack of goods that are waiting for you when you say No.

You will start to perceive the extent of marvellous good things you gain as compared to the bad ones you are leaving behind. As a result, restricting yourself from smoking will become a piece of cake.

Pause

Giving up things you do not like is easy and cigarettes is certainly one of them. Isn't it?

Feeling proud will be the side product of you being sober. It will become effortless to vanquish other habits. Altogether you will feel self-confident, self-assured, and self-reliant. You will be conquering your Life.

Every day you will feel evocative towards the grand step which made you happier. You'll start to count the days, weeks eventually the months along your journey. You'll come out as a speaker in your community to change others' lives as well.

Pause

You'll start to enjoy this journey. Keeping a record of the days of being an abstainer will become your diary to remember and to speak about. In time, keeping the record will not be necessary as you've conquered your habits and they no longer have the power over you. The rest of your life will be like a story to tell.

Habits are self-preserving. They are created in your mind. The power of your conscious mind is the only power that can dethrone them.

You are stronger than this habit. Now it's you versus the tobacco and you desire to come out as a winner. Patience, perseverance, calm, and relaxed determination are all your tools to fight this monster.

It's unshakable. One day at a time patiently. Counting each day as a success. Success will become habitual. And sooner, the love of success will become extensively grandiose than any habit has ever been.

Smoking Pros and Cons

You have been polluting your body for a very long time...perhaps your lungs are filled with toxins that are damaging your body and you have decided to give up smoking and that is why you are listening to this recording. You have taken the first step to loving yourself even more. And, that is amazing.

Pause

You will not put it off until tomorrow because that is what you have been trying to do for the past many years. Today is the day to quit smoking and be free from all the toxins to live a healthier and happier life.

Pause

Today, we are going to reinforce the desire to quit smoking, which is indeed good for your health and life. You will quit it once and for all. You know that smoking leads to cancer, which is painful and an expensive treatment. The very thought of

41

smoking a cigarette reminds you of cancer.

The thoughts about going through the series of tests, chemotherapy, losing hair makes your desire to quit smoking stronger. You cannot let yourself go through that just because one cigarette gives you pleasure for 5 minutes.

Pause

You are smart and intelligent who has started to love health and body more. And, an intelligent person analyses and sees the pros and cons of situations and things. What according to you are the pros and cons of smoking a cigarette. Perhaps it relaxes you and makes you calm for 5 minutes, but it does long term inner damage, which can come to the surface anytime in the form of a disease.

Longer Pause

The cons are bad breath, smelly hair, hands and clothes, inability to fall asleep, coughing, breathing problems, damage of lungs, tar and nicotine stains on teeth, and spending too much on cigarettes.

Longer Pause

And, before I move ahead with what I have to say, I would like you to make a mental commitment to yourself, promise yourself that you will never pick up a cigarette. Looking at all the cons and ill effects smoking brings, I am sure, you are going to quit smoking.

I would love you to understand that your powerful subconscious mind accepts everything that I say for your highest good. It does not and will not question and will only accept what you and I are telling him. Your promise and commitment to yourself goes straight into your subconscious mind and the thought becomes stronger and stronger.

Longer Pause

You are now committed to the decision of quitting smoking more than you have ever been before. Your imagination is much more stronger and powerful that your will. And the creative part of you, will help you imagine that you have destroyed all the packs of cigarettes at home and at work.

Pause

You put a fire to them for good. With every passing minute, you are thankful that you have been able to commit yourself to the decision that will change your life and health.

Pause

You will have a better relationship with yourself. You will smell good, there will not be any tar and tobacco stains on your teeth. You will smell fresh and your breath will be fresh.

Your health will start to improve with every passing day. You will breathe fresh air, you will enjoy every moment of your life breathing fresh and with more mental clarity. You will not have any guilt that you perhaps used to have after smoking a cigarette.

You will be free and happy.

Longer Pause

And these suggestions grow stronger and stronger with every passing minute, hour, and day. You are a non-smoker - and you are proud to be a non-smoker.

Road to Stopping Smoking

Life is about the conscious choices you make, and you often find yourself at different crossroads of life. This particular time, you realize that the road you have taken so far as a smoker is too long, and it goes on for many more miles.

Pause

You find yourself at yet another crossroads yet again. This time, you are considering taking a different path, but you are confused about which road to take, the road less taken, or the one which will change your life. You are demented about what changes this road is going to bring.

Pause

Here's a thought, let's continue walking on the path you have always taken. Let's explore this familiar path and see what's in the store for your life if you continue to smoke.

Keep walking this way. While sauntering along this old path, you will see things that are associated with smoking.

You will see those gifted ashtrays that are now overflowing with cigarette butts, you will see that thick cloud of smoke that gets into your lungs leaving you to wheeze, and gasp for breath along the way.

Longer Pause

You are now more conscious about how your clothes smell. It opens your eyes, and you start to keep your distance from non-smokers because your self-respect is taking a hit. You feel embarrassed about how awful you smell when you are with your friends.

Now that you are seeing yourself from a third person's perspective, you are also seeing other people smoke. They are wheezing, coughing, and gasping for breath the like you did.

Pause

While walking, you come across this familiar hospital, and you suddenly remember someone you know is admitted there. They are gasping for breath and desperately reaching out for a nebulizer. There is nothing you can do to help this person, so you are only able to feel sympathy for them.

As you continue walking along this path you see your future. You see that you are with your children, grandchildren, and babies who aren't allowed to hold in case you breathe on them and leave that stale unpleasant smell behind.

You are now short on money, but you are still trying to put it all together to buy a pack of cigarettes and smoking each one of them. It is a metaphor of how you are setting fire to not only your money but also your life. You are looking for each penny to buy poison and trying to kill yourself with that.

Longer Pause

When you see your hands, you are disgusted by them; they are stained because of the nicotine. They are now smelly, and your skin starts to feel nauseating and dirty. That irritating tickly cough just won't go away, so you are coughing and wheezing all the time.

Pause

You are now alienated from your group of friends, no one tries to approach you. In the office, you have to go outside to smoke and nobody accompanies you because of your toxic habit. Your co-workers start to step away from you, as you see them holding their nose trying not to inhale that stench.

How does it feel?

I am sure you are feeling bad about picking up this habit but you have decided to let go of it...isn't it?

Pause

You see your beautiful house ruined by the burn marks - the furniture has that unpleasant smell, and there are yellow stains on the wall because of the smoke, your heart breaks a little.

You walk towards the end of the road, and you see yourself lying on that hospital bed, like that friend you saw before. You are now scared for your life, as you see yourself fighting for the last breath. The things that you saw along your path are horrific, and they are now deeply carved in your mind forever.

Pause

Let's move on from the unpleasant imagination and feelings for now because none of them has happened to you yet, and it won't if you don't let it. You have reached that crossroads of life where you have to make a concrete decision of life or death. The fact that you are here today means a lot; that you want to correct your life; that you want to make these necessary changes to lead a happy life.

You have caught a glimpse of those vile things that could happen to you if you continued to walk on that road. I want to show you a glimpse of what life would be like if you take that new road to non-smoking.

Pause

The air is different on this road because it is clean and smoke-free. You get a crystal clear picture of everything, and you breathe in the pure air around you.

Notice how refreshing it is, it could last forever if you continue to walk on this new road. The fresh air fills your being with renewed energy and vitality. Even during this short span of non-smoking, you find that you're feeling better and healthier than ever before.

Longer Pause

Notice how your breathing has become easier than ever before. Your chest feels comfortable, and your throat is clearer. Your skin feels way better, and your fingers have no odour of cigarettes.

You start to smell good, as your clothes, skin, and hair are now clean. You now have that lovely, fresh, clean smell that is delicate, and you have that faint perfume by which people instantly recognize you.

Pause

If you observe keenly, you will realize that people are now idolizing you because you kept your word. People start hanging out with you again.

You are now a person of your words. Your conscious decision to quit smoking once and for all has brought people closer to you. The people you love are now close to you because you smell like integrity and trust.

On the new road, instead of a hospital, you see an entertainment centre where there is a sports complex or a gymnasium. Imagine some other place where you would enjoy keeping your body and mind healthy; where you will be yourself living your ambitions. Go to those places with your near and dear ones or with your peers that you have inspired by making a healthy choice to become, and remain a non-smoker for the rest of your life.

Pause

Your confidence level is so high that you rely on yourself instead of props or addictions. You become a confident and self-assured person. You have this wonderful feeling of achievement and attainment of wellbeing, after quitting smoking.

Your home has now become the most beautiful place on this earth for you. It is just so beautiful, and peaceful that you enjoy staying there.

You love this new you. You love it that you are a non-smoker now because it feels wonderful. It just increases your determination to be that way forever.

Keep the Motivation Going

Once you have lived that amazing non-smoker life, you are now motivated to live that life every day. Every day you feel better, healthier and the best version of yourself you have ever been. You radiate more energy, vitality, and you feel really good about yourself.

As you walk along the road of being a successful non-smoker, I wonder if you can see, sense, or feel yourself, after it's quite a long way past that crossroad of your life.

Imagine the future you, you have been a successful non-smoker, and you are feeling proud of yourself for being consistent.

Pause

The road is lovely, as it is full of flowers and greenery growing on both sides. You notice that being a non-smoker is paying off well, as endless opportunities are arising for you, and your confidence increasing because you feel so much better about yourself.

Do you realize how much money you have saved by not smoking? You could so much with that type of money. The small incremental savings daily will come back to you in heaps. You could purchase something special for yourself, perhaps a new outfit or something to compliment your home.

Pause

You could put in a deposit for a holiday, it doesn't matter what you do with the money, so long as it's something special for you. You deserve something amazing because you are special, you deserve to treat yourself, and you deserve to feel proud of yourself.

Longer Pause

You have become this wonderful human being who sticks by his/her words. You proved that you are consistent and you meant what you said when you stopped smoking completely.

You have come so far in life that I wonder if you could rewind for a second and go back to the time where you used to smoke.

Now, imagine that one of your toxic friends is there, a friend who smokes a lot and is offering you a fag.

Pause

You see them taking out a case of cigarettes. They are slowly but carefully unwrapping the cellophane from it. They are further opening the case and pulling the cigarettes out halfway to offer you one.

While this whole scene is taking place, you realize that the person is not your true friend. A true friend will never tempt you when you are so determined to remain a non-smoker.

Pause

Do you hear yourself say 'No' to cigarettes and meant it? Do you realize that your mind and body are rejecting cigarettes? Now that you know that cigarettes are like a poison to your system, you don't want them, you don't need them, so as a result, you don't have them.

Longer Pause

When you say 'No' to cigarettes, an amazing thing happens, you experience a wonderful feeling flowing into your being. It fills your very existence with pride, confidence, and a sense of achievement.

You feel fresh, so you say 'No' to cigarettes, and you mean it. You decline the offer because you're a non-smoker now, and that's the way you prefer to be.

Every day you feel better and healthier and happier, you have more confidence and more vitality and you feel good because you are a non-smoker now. You are a non-smoker and that's the way you do prefer to be.

Pause

This feeling only gets stronger. You become more determined and motivated which makes you feel better, happier, healthier, and fitter than ever before.

Now that you are a non-smoker, you prefer to be one forever. These suggestion grow stronger every day, as they become more profound, powerful, and more important to you.

Smoking Cessation

Imagine that you are entering a special room. Now, when you look around, you see that your room is filled with beautiful lights and wonderful colors. Do you notice how your room is furnished and the air is clean around you?

Now, imagine that the air you are breathing is filled with thousands of tiny molecules of clean and pure energy. Every molecule penetrates deeply into your chest and flows right into your lungs because the air quality is pure.

Pause

Now, you see yourself from another perspective, as a non-smoker. Did you notice how much better you look now that you've stopped smoking? Your complexion is clearer, your breath is fresh, and your mouth tastes cleaner. You have more energy and vitality, your eyes are sparkling, and so you look, and feel better than you've ever felt before.

You feel relaxed, self-assured, and very confident about yourself. All your senses are sharpened, your food tastes better, your sense of smell is heightened, your mind is clearer, even your circulation is improved by giving up smoking.

Longer Pause

From this moment you are a non-smoker. You don't ever want to smoke because you don't like it and therefore you have quit smoking. Smoking was your thing in the past; it's something you used to do. You are a non-smoker now, and you are proud to be a NON-SMOKER.

When you are with other people who smoke you become extremely consciously of the stale and unpleasant smell of tobacco coming from them. You can smell that stale tobacco on their clothes, hair, breath, and even on the skin of every smoker that you come across.

Pause

You're disgusted by that stale smell of tobacco, it makes you feel nauseous, and the thought that you've been inhaling that poison into your body makes you feel sick, and that is exactly why you prefer NOT to think about cigarettes at all. It is also the reason that you made a firm commitment to yourself, to never smoke again. From this moment forward you have no desire, no need, no want, to ever smoke again.

Pause

You have created your world where there is nothing called smoking, at least not for you.

Smoking was part of the old you, the dependent you, but this new you have more confidence. You are now in more control of how you feel, you feel happier and calmer than ever before.

Giving up smoking **makes** you feel more confident, it is a sign that you are in control of your mind, body, and your health. You enjoy this feeling of being in control. You love how that toxic part of you has vanished into thin air, you are now an ex-smoker, and you are PROUD to be an ex-smoker. You are proud of the fact that you could overcome something that you were struggling with for so long.

Pause

I suggest you to project your mind into the future, and imagine those six beautiful smoke-free months that have gone by where you neither had, nor wanted a cigarette.

These past six relaxing smoke-free months, you enjoyed being a non-smoker. You're feeling healthier, happier, cleaner, and more in control of your mind, body, and health.

Longer Pause

Imagine that you are allowing someone to come into this scene and that they are offering you a cigarette. They are offering the cigarette to you and your immediate reflex is a firm 'No'. You say

'No' to the cigarettes because your mind and body reject them. You don't want them or you don't feel the need to have them, so your mind decided not to have them.

When you say 'No', you mean it. You know that cigarettes are poisonous to your system, your mind. Your body rejects them as soon as the thought comes of a cigarette.

Pause

Saying 'No' to cigarette feels good because you love being in control of your mind. Now that you are in complete control of your body, mind, and your health, you are easily controlling your urges. You love being a non-smoker because it makes you feel good. It gives you confidence and control of your body.

Pause

Over the next few days and weeks you're going to be drinking lots of water because it will help you flush the nicotine out of your system, once and for all.

You love the taste of water and you know it help in flushing out the toxins and gives your face a beautiful glow. With every passing day, your mind becomes even stronger and you become even more in control of your health and urges.

Pause

You drink at least 8 to 9 glasses of water everyday

You are now a non-smoker and enjoy this amazing feeling of being free from the toxic substance. It's so refreshing to completely eliminate tobacco from your system. In no time, you will start to see the positive results in your breathing, throat, sense of taste and smell, and skin.

Appreciate Yourself

It would be great if you were appreciated by everyone all the time. It would be so good to be liked by all. Imagine never getting criticized or being treated unfairly by a single individual.

But what's not great is how you feel down all the time to anybody around you. It is not such a great feeling when your happiness seems to be out of your grip. Your happiness is your own responsibility and you can be the one who has control over it.

Pause

You are not seeking perfection, but only the sense of being a healthy human. You understand that perfection or perfectionism is unattainable.

And those who blindly run after it are only going to end up in disappointment. The craving for perfection is only going to consign one to a life of failure and frustration.

Your understanding of this is as why you will always have your humanity as your strength.

Longer Pause

You need to try to understand that there are people out there who like you for the way you are; with all your humanity and all your strengths. They see you as a fantastic person who is great, today, just being yourself. What can you possibly do about the few who don't appreciate you?

It will not matter to them even if you change your hair, your habits, your size, shape, clothes or your behaviour. Some people appreciate you today with everything that you have. Some believe that you need no change and cannot be better than this. Some might start appreciating you tomorrow or a week later.

Pause

The only thing that should matter to you is that you are honest to yourself. You should be the one who appreciates all your strengths and cherish and nurture them. Learn what you're good at and rejoice in it. You also need to understand and be just as honest about your flaws.

Pause

Try and work hard towards fixing anything that can be remedied. And as to any flaw you find no solution to, remember that there is no use by being overwhelmed or paralyzed by it. Make peace with yourself and your nature. Always work in the direction of progress to fix any flaws you feel, even if it's not speedy. The will to change is what will lead to change.

Longer Pause

Some people will think of you as a wonderful person while some won't. These opinions won't matter to you when you have embraced yourself. When you know all your strengths and work on changing the inescapable for yourself, you are at ease with the judgments of others. You work on yourself with a cool head and a calm heart.

Pause

No matter where you are, with friends or family, you welcome both praise and criticism. It is great when somebody sees your strengths and agrees with you. It is also fine for people to disagree and not appreciate you. It is only human to make mistakes.

You know yourself with your humanity and strength. You accept you need to work on yourself quietly. The opinions of others hold no surprise for you anymore. People either agree and accept you or let them be wrong.

Pause

This day onwards, you only wish to eat food that is healthy and right for you. You eat the right quantities, at the right time for the right reasons. You are completely content and satisfied with your choice. You are getting slimmer, fitter, healthier and happier by the day. Not to forget, even more gorgeous.

Today, tomorrow, every day you feel good about yourself even from within. You are forever at ease with yourself. You like yourself and feel happy, settled, secure and satisfied naturally. You are more confident, optimistic, cool, calm and comfortable being yourself.

Sleep Better

And as you continue to listen to me, your imagination further expands and you imagine a brightly lit room. The room has a window through which you can you see the sunshine coming. Because the room is lit, you can easily see the walls and ceiling of the room with your thoughts everywhere. You can notice what thoughts keep you up and what thoughts keep you from falling asleep.

Longer Pause

For good health, it's important to sleep better and when you sleep well at night, you wake up feeling happy and fresh. Your brain functions better. So, to be able to sleep well at night, you need to clear all the thoughts from the walls, so that the room looks clean and as the Sun goes down, you start to feel relaxed and calmer.

Look around and carefully notice what all is written on the walls. Do they even serve any purpose?

Pause

Perhaps they are the thoughts from the past or future that stops you from falling asleep in the present.

There is no point in having these thoughts. Isn't it?

Longer Pause

The room looks chaotic because there is so much on the walls, floor, and the ceiling. What is the point in having such a room?

So, you decide to paint the walls new. Before that, you are going to scrape off all the thoughts with a sandpaper. You magically see the sand paper appearing in front of you. You take it in your hands and start scraping the walls, floor, and ceiling now.

Longer Pause

And once you have scraped off the thoughts from the floor, ceiling, and walls, you feel tired and relaxed.

So, you relax for a moment in the room and as you relax, you notice that the Sun starts to go down…and you start to feel even more relaxed.

The room has started to get a bit dark because the Sun light is moving away and in a moment, you will notice a big paint bucket with paint brushes and rollers appearing magically in the room.

Pause

And, with the powerful imagination, your start to paint the walls black so that it gets dark in the room and you start to feel even more sleepier and drowsier.

Start painting the walls black. Take the paint brush and start painting the walls and ceiling now.

Pause

That's right. Now start painting the ceiling black...

Longer Pause

Now, imagine putting a black rug on the floor, which is fuzzy and soft to touch. And as you feel the rug beneath your feet.

Longer Pause

And as you do that...you feel some weight has been lifted off your body and you instantly feel relaxed and calm.

Pause

There are no thoughts on the floor or ceiling or floor and all you can notice is the darkness all around you because of no Sunshine outside of the room, black painted walls and ceiling and black rug.

Longer Pause

The room now looks absolutely black from all sides...

It's comfy and you are not distracted...

You now allow yourself to count back from 5 down to 0...and with each count down...you will be twice as relaxed and twice as deep.

5...feeling relaxed
4...going deeper and deeper
3...relaxing more and more..
2...entering a deep state of relaxation
1...calmer and deeper

Affirmations for Sleep

I would now like you to repeat the suggestions after me..

It's so much more easier to let go of every thought about past and future every night (4-5 seconds pause)

I close my eyes and paint the room black in my mind when I want to sleep (4-5 seconds pause)

With every brush stroke, it's easier for me to let go and drift into a peaceful sleep (4-5 seconds pause)
I feel drowsier when I imagine yourself painting the room black (4-5 seconds pause)

My mind is relaxed and my thoughts slow down as soon as I hit the bed (4-5 seconds pause)

Stop smoking II

Congratulations! I'm very proud of you that you have made this important decision in your life. By listening to me, you have decided to become a non-smoker. If you pay close attention, you will realize that you always wanted to quit smoking, and that is what makes this very special, as you have finally decided to honour your body and quit smoking.

Pause

Your body barely liked you for treating it so badly; your toxic habits were hurting your body and you without your knowledge. It is beautiful that you are now finally doing something good for yourself. Nicotine is not the addictive part because if it was then people would have been addicted to alternatives like the nicotine patch or the nicotine gum. If it was addictive, then someone I would be doing this hypnosis therapy to make people quit the gum or the patch. Till now, it has never happened and I can ensure that it never will.

I wonder why people keep smoking, is it because it's a habit? But then again, what is a habit? It's when you automatically think about doing something and simply responding to a thought. Well, if that's the case then you don't have to do that anymore because you are free from smoking.

Pause

You subconsciously know that smoking is just your way of responding to a destructive thought. You should know that your thoughts have no power over you because when you look back you will realize that you have thought about doing thousands of things and then simply decided not to do them.

Pause

Remember the time when you decide to buy something but then changed your decision not to buy it because you thought that the money would be better spent on something else? It is the same thing with cigarettes. If you think about it, when it comes to spending your money, it is always better spent on something else than cigarettes.

Pause

Always remember that there is something better to do than smoke. It is not the nicotine in the cigarettes that are addictive, but it's the poison that is. There is only a small amount of poison in each cigarette, but even that tends to build up until your body becomes affected by it and you become sick. Sometimes it becomes a major illness like cancer, heart disease, or emphysema, and other times, it is something like a cough or bronchitis. You know the consequences so you have decided not to let any of those things happen to you. You are now strong and you have made a very strong decision to not let that happen to you.

Pause

You are very stubborn about sticking to being a non-smoker and to let go of all the worries and sickness associated with cigarettes. As you are grasping that fact, you are becoming free, so all of your urges start to fade away.

You have taken complete control, you are not going to allow yourself to be weak that will eventually make you sick, a mere thought. Have you thought about how this thought came into your mind? It's not like you were walking down the street one day and this idea popped into your head out of nowhere.

Pause

You must have got this idea from somewhere or it is also possible that you would have seen someone else smoking, and that idea clung on to your mind. You saw some else do it and somehow you thought it would be a good idea if you did it too, but have you wondered where did they get this idea from? If you think about it, everyone smokes for one reason - someone must have made some compelling points and sold it to them!

Today, you smoke because it is one of the most successful marketing plans in the history of the world. It started years ago when America entered WWII, and everyone was so sold on the idea of cigarettes that even the government was buying them to give it to our brave men and women who were fighting a war. As a result, most of those people came back with the smoking habit.

Longer Pause

We get influenced by the people we admire the most and that why we look up to our parents, role models, celebrities, and try to replicate their actions. Smoking is one of those traits that you pick up from these people and just because they smoke, you smoke too. This habit is just handed down to you and you take it because you want to look cool in front of your peers.

If you go down your memory to our previous conversation about WWII, you will realize that comparatively, people who die of smoking are more than the people who died in the great wars. These corporate companies are easily advertising this product for you to break down and once you fall for it, it's all over for you. Once you realize that it's all a setup, you are on to them and their advertising campaign no longer affects you.

Now you regret, you regret being sold that pack of lies in the form of your "stress buster". You now know that each pack of cigarettes is a pack of lies and smoking is now simply something you "used to do". You are free from the chain of a toxic decision you made a long time ago.

It will feel so good to be free, free from all the pain, and the worry. Every time you find yourself slipping, you will remember that there is always something better to do than to smoke a pack of lies. Now that you have quit smoking for good, you will have time to experience so many fun and interesting things to do.

Pause

The information that I'm giving you now is stored in your conscious and subconscious mind, so you no longer can accept poisoning yourself for any reason. You turn away from any form of tobacco, so you are free. Free from the urge and that poisonous chain.

You feel free, you feel so free and relaxed that you don't feel the need to smoke while going back after work. This day is your special day; you can consider it as important as your birthday or anniversary. When you look back, you will feel content because this is the day when you finally took back the control over your body.

Longer Pause

That implies, now you are in complete control of your body, you have finally got what you were longing for, for so long. Now that you are in control, you regret the fact that some poisonous substances controlled you for long and you didn't even know it. But instead of dwelling on your past mistakes, you should be celebrating the fact that no matter what happens; you will never lose control over your body again. You should feel because now you have all the time in the world and you can always do something better with it rather than poisoning yourself with cigarettes.

Remember that smoking is no longer connected to your life in any way, and all of those old self-harming connections are broken up with, completely. All those activities you used to do while smoking will now be even better because you are healthier now and there will not be any embarrassment, worry, or frustration of cigarettes! Now if you watch TV, visit a friend, or simply chinwag on the telephone, you are not worried about cigarettes.

They were dirty (filthy) and they made you sick, but now everything goes better with the health and confidence you find as a non-smoker. You are free from all the frustration and now smoking is simply something that you "used to do". You are now free because there is always something better to do than smoke.

There is always a gut feeling that your subconscious mind warns you about and you had that feeling about quitting smoking.

You always know that you would quit smoking one day and it worked so congratulations! This is not a feeling that you have just for a day and then you go back to square one, you have accomplished something that you will cherish for the rest of your life.

Longer Pause

You are free from smoking for today and the rest of your life. When you decided to quit smoking you took the initiative to quit all of your reasons as well. You made a great package deal. You made a great trade! You traded something toxic for something priceless and healthy.

If you think about it, no amount of money can add a day or two to your life; it completely depends on the quality of life you aspire to lead.

Pause

Do you realize how many people wish that they could trade something for more time, a longer life? You have traded smoking for something precious, a longer life. You are now going to live a higher quality of life. This new life of yours is going to be filled with time, money, and self-respect. It is going to give you more vitality and confidence to take on the world.

By now you should realize that if you don't have your health, you don't have anything. You have made a jackpot deal where you are trading something you don't want at all for something that will end up giving you happiness and health. Besides, now you have plenty of time to enjoy every minute of it. Remember your mantra as you make these new changes, smoking is simply something that you "used to do".

Longer Pause

If you broaden your perspective a little bit, you will realize that there is always something better to do than smoking your lungs out. Think about your past trauma, think about all the things you went through, you would never go back to the old ways since they are simply toxic. Smoking is never a good idea, it causes pain and you simply traded it for something better, good health. No matter how much withdrawal tests you, never go back to smoking, and always remember that you can handle your life without cigarettes.

Longer Pause

You are too good for smoking; you are so stubborn that you will reject a fag at any given circumstance. Always remember that there is something better to do than smoking and keep saying it to you like it is a mantra. The withdrawal from smoking will keep you free and in control forever.

Pause

Think about it, every time you want to smoke, drink water because having a drink of water is better, even chewing a piece of gum is better than smoking. Doing anything other than smoking (as long as it is not illegal, immoral, or fattening) is better than smoking.

You are in control; you handle these situations effectively like a boss. You are now in complete control of your body, so you will no longer poison it with that toxic habit. You are simply going to turn your back on all of that poison and as a result, your body will reward you with health. Your mind will reward you by thinking more clearly since the smoke has cleared.

Pause

Emotionally, you will feel better because you are free from all the worrying and stress of smoking. Smoking is simply something that you used to do. You traded it away for something priceless - life, health, self-confidence, and peace of mind. Congratulate yourself now because you are a non-smoker and you are going to be that way for the rest of your life. You are now least bothered by people who smoke around you and when they do, it only makes you proud of yourself. You feel proud of the fact that you are now in complete control of your body (even though you might feel a little sorry for them).

Longer Pause

When you are around smokers, the smoke and fire will not affect you in any way because you can enjoy the company of others that smoke, but not want it at all for yourself. You will always feel a little better (inside and out) knowing that you are back in control. You can be proud of yourself because cigarettes cannot push you around anymore. You are proud to be a non-smoker and you are going to be a non-smoker for the rest of your long healthy life.

Repeat this silently to yourself as I say it out loud, "I am now a non-smoker, and I'm going to be a non-smoker for the rest of my life." (Compound it 15 times).

Longer Pause

From this moment on, you are a non-smoker. You feel better than ever before and you are going to feel better yet, as your lungs continue to become healthier because you have gotten rid of all the tobacco poison.

Pause

You are thoroughly done with all the toxicity and the smell as there is a part of you that always hated it. You have always hated it because it is filthy, dirty, and it makes you sick to your stomach. You refuse to debate your decision because your mind is now made up. You are stubborn about quitting because when you think about cigarettes, you know that you will make that mistake never again.

Longer Pause

Now, if for any reason in your life, you think that you might want a cigarette, all you have to do is take a deep breath and as you exhale, just say to yourself, "There is always something better to do than smoke". Let yourself have that feeling of being in control. Let's try that exercise right now, take a deep breath, and as you exhale, say to yourself, "There is always something better to do than smoke." Notice how good it feels to be free from that old toxic habit. Add patterns that you can use if you have time. You are here today because you have made up your mind completely to become a non-smoker. You want to quit because you can no longer let cigarettes control your life.

You are now motivated. You are motivated to let go of the pain and suffering that comes with smoking. You are willing to face the world without smoking. You are hit by the fact that smoking is a real poison and a threat to your happiness. We will now try breaking all of the links that you have made between smoking and other things. Remember?

There is always something better to do than smoking, when you are bored, stressed, etc.

Your desire for cigarettes is fading away to nothing and all the connections are completely dissolved. These new changes that you have been implementing into your life have changed you into a new person, a non-smoker. Your reactions to cigarettes as a non-smoker are opposite; you are irritated and a little revolted even by the smell of it. Non-smokers handle their feelings and emotions without cigarettes and react differently.

Pause

It is one of the many benefits that come with quitting cigarettes, you are not worrying about them, you are wearing fresh-smelling clothes, your breath, and health is way better. "I'm now a non-smoker and I'm going to be a non-smoker for the rest of my life!" When you are around others that smoke it will make you feel good to know that you are in control of your life.

Pause

If you ever have even the slightest thought of having a cigarette, all you have to do is take a deep breath, hold it, and slowly exhale and you will be back in control, feeling good about your new life.

White Light Meditation

With your eyes closed, picture a white light emerging through you forehead; reaching and relaxing every nerve, fiber, muscle in your body. When you think about your forehead, it smoothens and relaxes.

The light goes on to relax your eyes, face muscles and jaw. The place where all your tension and stress gather is your jaw. It is fine for you to open your mouth a bit to relax it. The white light reaches your neck and then your chest, relaxing them on its way. Every breath relaxes you more and more. It is the sound of my voice that relaxes you. You are letting go of any other sound that is unimportant to you.

Pause

The white light moves further down to your arms and hands. Every muscle relaxes slowly. It is perfectly fine for you to feel you palm warming up and a tingling sensation in your fingertips. You are finding it difficult to lift your arms as they feel heavier but much relaxed. As you now take a deep breath, your leg muscles loosen up all the way down to your toes. Your entire body has now lightened and become relaxed.

Longer Pause

You are now going to visualize a peaceful, special place for yourself. It is perfectly fine for you to choose anything for yourself, be it a beach or a mountain. You now notice a 10 step staircase that takes you down to this place.

Every step getting closer to this place doubles your relaxation. Standing on the 10th step, you drift deeper and deeper – step 9,8,7 and so on. As you slowly get of step one, you have finally arrived in you special place. In this special place, you are isolated from any disturbances.

Your mind is peaceful. You can come to this place anytime and let go of you daily life stress and tension. In this special place, you are always going to have a sense of peace and calm, well-being and any sign of stress will completely bounce off of you.

Pause

You are taking this journey of change with my voice, becoming more and more peaceful with every breath. The sound of my voice relaxes you.

You are now focusing on your eyes. Your eyes have reached to a stage of relaxation where they feel only like a piece of skin. In a few moments I will ask you to open your eyes on my count, but it will be in vain. You will notice that your eyes seem to be stuck together, unable to open no matter how much you try. Now, 1,2,3 – I am asking you to try and open your eyes. Try a little harder. Now, I want you to shift your focus and go in deeper into hypnosis.

Your mind is now open to my voice which has an ever increasing effect over your way of thinking and feeling.

Today is the first day of your non-smoking life. You have now become a non-smoker. This decision is fuelled by all the right reasons and a motivation to rid your body of this habit. You realize that giving up this habit makes space for you to take part in healthy habits such as drinking lots of water.

Pause

Your decisions let you lose an enemy and gain health. You will be successful in this endeavor just as you have been in your past ones. You are now the person you always wanted to be – a non-smoker. From now onwards, the thought of smoking cigarettes will repulse you.

Longer Pause
You understand that it is a disgusting habit that impeded your breathing. It also took away your

ability to relax, creating boredom and reducing your self-esteem. But you have now had enough of this sickening habit that fills your system with dirt.

The smell of cigarettes has now become positively revolting for you. Imagine throwing away a pack of cigarettes. You need to be rid of this poison. So today, you are going to go home and clean out nay traces of your smoking habits.

Pause

You will find it refreshing to have every cigarette thrown out and clothes washed out to clean the smell. You can do all this because you are now a NON-SMOKER.
We are now going to place a new picture in your head. In this picture, you are standing in a spring flower meadow surrounded by Hyacinths, primroses, bluebells and daffodils - all the flowers that you love.

Longer Pause

You can also see English castle surrounded by water and a moat at some distance. Your curiosity asks you to explore it. You walk to the castle, open a creaking door and find yourself standing in the dark. Only a stream of light enters the castle through a turret. In this band of light, you see dirt.

Pause

You decide to pick up the spicket and scrubbing brush lying there and clean it all. You watch all the dirt go down the drain as you scrub and wash the walls. It takes a lot of water but you finally clean it and go back out into the meadows. As you step out, you are amazed by the awakening of your senses.

You can feel the fresh air blowing over your skin. You can sell the sweet smell of all the flowers. You now feel proud of yourself for putting in the work to clean up and you now lay down to rest and take a nap.

Tomorrow, when you wake up you will start your first full day of being a non-smoker. You feel great that you made the decision with all the right reasons and are carrying it through.

Pause

With every breath you take in, you trust your ability to set goals and achieve the. You are now a non-smoker. Try and visualize your life an year from now. You have finally made it.

It came very easily to you once you made a motivated decision. You realize that you have saved money for yourself in this last year and you give yourself a treat that day. This is all because you have put yourself in the centre of your universe. You are the best.

Longer Pause

You can now visualize the healing white light passing through every nerve and muscle and healing everything. You are now getting cleansed. Imagine that white light now passing on from you to those close to you – healing and cleaning them all. You are all the light.

Pause

You now have to remember this feeling of being a non-smoker and the white light. You want to be the light. You wish to be healthy. You are now a non-smoker who is healing his/her body with every breath he/she takes.

So now onwards, when you put your head on your pillow to sleep, remember that you will have the best sleep through the night and wake up fresh. You are going to be relaxed and fantastic. The first thing that you will say to yourself is – I am a non-smoker.

Sleep Reprogramming

As you continue to listen to me, you know that in your mind, there is a beautiful place, a place like beach, where your subconscious mind can program itself. The programming of mind will help you return to the ability you were born with. You an naturally fall asleep and stay asleep throughout the night, each and every night.

Your powerful subconscious mind can be much faster than what I say and has the ability to interpret and absorb the information. It keeps the information for a long time. And as I speak, your conscious mind can drift away to the beach. The beautiful beach with grainy brown sand and blue waters. The waves crashing against the seashore. And as you conscious mind drifts there, your subconscious accepts all that I am saying.

And your vast subconscious mind goes far ahead of me to act on every healthy things for you to sleep peacefully and better, every night. The more you listen to me, the more strongly every breath restores you to a peaceful sleep every night.

You let your subconscious mind know that how much you appreciate deep sleep as it allows you to function fully the next day, at home or at work. You tell your subconscious mind now that how important restful sleep is to you.

Longer Pause

You also tell your subconscious mind the bad effects of not sleeping on time and fully. It leads to crankiness, snapping at people, irritability, lack of focus and attention, low energy, and mental confusion.

Pause

And, allow your subconscious mind to understand the consequences of not sleeping well.

Longer Pause

Let your subconscious mind know what is it that you want it to do so that every morning you are awaken feeling fresh.

Tell your mind that you want to awaken each day feeling rested and refreshed. That, you want a restful, peaceful, and deep sleep every night.

You wish to be awaken every day feeling absolutely wonderful, positive, and motivated. You want to feel happy, energetic, and fully recharged. For this, of course, you want to be able to fall asleep faster and get up feeling recharged and refreshed.

Now, allow your subconscious mind to know all the benefits of sleeping on time and deeply.

Longer Pause

Your subconscious mind knows and accepts your new goal to sleep better and if there is an old pattern of sleeping less, that will simply fade away.

The part of your powerful creative subconscious mind monitors every word I say and locks in every positive idea for you. And, it has the ability to go deeper into your mind and reprograms everything for your highest good.

And, because you want to be able to get up feeling absolutely refreshed and recharged, you practice taking 3 deep breaths. Each breath will relax you and ground you. As you settle into your bed, you close your eyes and take three deep breaths. While you breathe in and breathe out, you practice imagining the color of positivity inhaling and the color of negativity exhaling.

That's right.

And, then imagining painting the walls and ceiling of the room completely black. This way you will start to feel drowsier and sleepier. And all through the sleep hours, you sleep peacefully and deeply.

Every muscle in your body relaxes and you can feel the fuzzy and soft black rug beneath your feet, giving you a beautiful and relaxed feeling.

Pause

And as you do so, you also say the word "Sleep Now" that your subconscious mind will know and recognize and because of all the reprograming, it will make you fall asleep.

Sleep Now is your magic word from now on and as you relax in your bed and preparing to fall asleep, you say the word as many times as possible, till you feel the need to fall asleep.

Pause

Everytime you repeat the word – Sleep Now to yourself, you automatically drift into a natural and peaceful sleep. And with every time you say it, you become more and more relaxed and calmer.

You enjoy restful and deep sleep. The next morning, you wake up feeling refreshed and relaxed.

Pause

You will be woken up by your Subconscious mind if at night there is any emergency or you feel the need to use the restroom.

And, you can go back to sleep by repeating the word – Sleep Now.

Everyone is born with a natural ability to sleep and that is why babies sleep and new borns sleep for upto 20 hours in a day. Sleep is not something to be learnt. It is natural and it will come to you when you allow it to.

Pause

And as you get into the bed, you imagine a beautiful blanket that is fuzzy, warm, and colorful covering you from all sides. This makes you feel comforted and safe at night. The colorful blanket has all the colors like orange, red, yellow, green, blue, violet, and white.

Imagine all the colors on you and around you NOW.

Pause

These colors swirls together all around you, over you, through you, keeping you warm and safe.

And as you look at each color in the swirl, you notice drifting further down in a beautiful state of relaxation.

In you mind again, repeat the magic word – Sleep Now.

Your mind has been totally re-programed for refreshing and full night's sleep. When you sleep better, you are less stressed and more relaxed and can easily handle day to day issues with your wise mind.

For that you do not have to pick up a cigarette. You only have to have a glass of water, imagine taking deep breaths, and believe in yourself…that you can do it.

You are a non-smoker

You love yourself and your health

You look forward to having a restful sleep every night.

You believe in yourself.

You can do it.

Longer Pause

Stop Smoking with Self Hypnosis

You can use this process anytime when you are sitting in a chair. You do not have to listen to the whole recording to do this. You only have to know this process and you can self-hypnotize yourself at any time.

Begin this process by finding a comfortable place where you feel relaxed. Practice what I am saying in your mind as if you are doing this.

Pause

I am now sitting or lying here, with my feet side by side and my hands resting loosely. My head is supported, and I'm aware of all the sounds around me, however, they don't disturb me because for the next thirty minutes or so there is absolutely nothing at all for me to do but relax and let go.

Pause

As I begin to relax and listen to the sound of my voice, I know that from time to time my mind may get distracted, but that's fine. It's fine because right now, there is nothing else on my mind, I'm nothing but relaxed, and even if my mind begins to think of other, unpleasant thoughts, the words that I speak will penetrate deeply into my subconscious mind. Soon, my words will become my thoughts, and my thoughts become my new reality because I've made a conscious decision to become a non-smoker. I have made that decision and I intend to stick by it as I don't want to let myself down.

I'm aware of the weight and the shape of my feet and my legs. My feet are becoming so heavy, so heavy and so comfortably relaxed, so heavy and comfortable they just don't want to move. My feet now feel as heavy as lead, like two lead weights and they just don't want to move at all.

Longer Pause

My eyes are also becoming heavy along with my feet, my eyes are drifting so hard that they just want to close. They feel like onion skins, their layers are so heavy yet so comfortable. I feel so relaxed that when I close my eyes I'm aware of patterns of light filtering through my closed lids - the patterns of light; perhaps the colours like orange, pink even red. My eyes are becoming heavier and heavier, but I'm so comfortably relaxed they just don't want to open at all.

Pause

As I notice the heaviness on my lids, my hands and arms are relaxing more and more. I'm noticing the warmth in the palms of my hands, it is a lovely warm feeling, that tingling feeling in the palms of my hands and the heaviness is spreading from my fingertips up to the top of my shoulders.

It is making me comfortably tired and relaxes that I just want to drift away to a more comfortable place. This feeling is just so serene that it makes my whole body comfortable and makes me want to drift far away. It is taking me down to a wonderful place, the place I feared the most, it is taking myself deep inside me.

Pause

In the creative part of my subconscious mind, I have so many rooms, I can explore wherever I choose to. It was my conscious decision to become healthy again and that's one of the reasons that I have stopped smoking. Now onwards, I'm going to treat my body like it's a new day because I've had enough of abusing my body, filling my lungs with black smoke, tar, nicotine, and all the poisons contained in cigarettes. Starting today, I decide to be healthy, I want to breathe clean air and go back to my natural state.

Pause

I now realize that I wasn't always a smoker, there was once a wonderful time when I didn't even think about cigarettes, and I intend to back to those times. I want to recapture the feelings of health and vitality, of feeling clean and even disliking that stale unpleasant smell on those around me who smoked.

Longer Pause

I can recall how people looked silly to me when they were breathing in fumes into their own body and then breathing them out like silly children dicing with death. They seemed like they were taunting death and were saying, come and get me if you dare.

Now when I look back I think to myself, was I one of those people? Was I also behaving in a childish manner thinking that I was immortal?

Pause

I have done my research and now I know all the facts about smoking and until now I was choosing to ignore them, but not anymore. As I'm becoming more conscious now of how I treat my body, how could I have done that to me? It's never too late, but I won't put it off a moment longer, I'm a non-smoker now and I have decided that's all I need.

Pause

Going ahead, I might face some difficult moments, but I'm prepared for them, that's how much focused I'm. I'm willing to pay the price to stay determined because it is very hard to resist.

I have a very strong will, I will not fall for temporary temptations because I have my consciousness, that conscious mind has decided to be a non- smoker I'm not weak-willed - I'm me - I'm a strong person with a will and a mind of my own and that makes me proud.
Longer Pause

No more sneaking around to smoke cigarettes when other non-smokers are around, that part of my life is long gone, I'm conscious of the stale unpleasant smell of tobacco on people who smoke, and I notice it on their clothes, on their hair, on their breath and even on the skin of people who smoke. I'm glad that I don't smell dirty anymore, I'm so proud of myself because I did it.

I did it all by myself, no one else but me. It's such a wonderful feeling to be free of that old addiction of the mind. I'm now free from all the addictions and I'm fine.

I'm going to remember some happy memories of a time when I felt so proud and confident. As that memory begins to resurface, I'll take a couple of deep, refreshing breaths, and touch

my earlobe with my hand to remind myself of how good I feel.
(Pause for a moment to allow a memory to come forward, and then touch the earlobe with hand).

Longer Pause

I can feel wonderful anytime I want to, I have all the confidence that I need to succeed, and if the thought of a cigarette enters my mind, I'll pause and take a couple of deep, refreshing breaths, and touch my earlobe with my hand. This will allow all those good feelings to come back to me anytime I want.

I'm now going to double the joy by squeezing my earlobe and by counting to five. I'm slowly lifting my hand and I'm squeezing my earlobe meanwhile I take some deep breaths continuing to count 1...2...3...4...5

Pause

I'm going to the creative part of my subconscious mind to explore those rooms, and in each one of those rooms are associations that I have with smoking. One of the rooms may involve smoking whilst talking to friends and I'm going into that room to get a sense of talking to my friends without a cigarette.

Instead of smoking, I'll take a couple of deep, refreshing breaths, while squeezing my earlobe and counting to five in my head. Those good feelings will break any association with smoking whilst talking to friends.

Pause

There is another room which also contains an association with smoking; it is after a heavy meal or with a drink. I'm going into that room to get a sense of finishing a meal or a drink without a cigarette, instead of smoking I'll take a couple of deep, refreshing breaths, squeeze my earlobe and count to five in my head and those good feelings will break any association with smoking.

Longer Pause

I will continue this process and I will search every room to break all my old associations with smoking. I will replace them with my new anchor and when I'm done with all the rooms, I will go for another round and then finally come back to the present time. While coming back, I will bring the determination and motivation that I need to succeed. I open my eyes feeling refreshingly alert and happy to be a non-smoker. All sensations of heaviness will leave my body as it returns to normal conscious awareness.

The Time Distortion Method

You are deeply relaxed, and the suggestions that you are now going to hear are going to have a lasting impact on your subconscious mind. You will keenly listen to every word I say even if your mind wanders sometimes. Right now, nothing else matters, nothing is more important than this beautiful relaxed feeling that you are experiencing.

Pause

At this point, you don't care about anything in this world, you understand that nobody wants anything, nobody needs anything and there is absolutely nothing at all for you to do except relax and let go. You just want to enjoy the feelings that are being generated within you.

Pause

Your eyes are beginning to feel heavy and sleepy, you could move but you just can't be bothered to, and you know how it is when you're just drifting off to sleep, your body sometimes makes an involuntary movement before letting go.

Your mind can wander away, the images can float into your mind and it's as though you become immersed in those images and dreams take over. When you are awake, you're well-rested, completely refreshed, and ready to begin a new day.

Longer Pause

What about those bad dreams? Where do they go? If you think of them as soon as you wake up, then you may remember elements of the dream. If the dream was vivid, you may remember every detail of it and only to forget at a later time.

The memory of those dreams remains in your subconscious mind, at an unconscious level that we surely won't recall every single dream that we ever had. Those dreams that seemed to last for so long, but in reality, were each just a few minutes short.

Pause

It is just as it is in hypnosis. We can travel forward, backward, or even sideways in our dreams where we're someone else completely. As you continue to listen to my voice, you are falling asleep.

My voice will be guiding you to a special sort of sleep, where you are not asleep but you are also not awake. You can hear my voice but your mind is just wandering off to its special thoughts that are led by things you unconsciously process.

Longer Pause

I would like to suggest that you experience a wonderful dream in your sleep, so go forward in time to six months from now where you're in a beautiful garden bordered with a mixture of colourful flowers and herbs that send out their perfume into the warm summer air. The air is still and birds are singing sweet songs in the trees.

There is a huge archway in your garden that is covered in jasmine and a little path leading through to a lovely ornamental pond with a rockery and a waterfall. You can hear the sound of the water hitting those rocks and splashing softly into the pond.

Pause

You realize how beautiful this place is and it is even better now because your sense of smell has improved, and the fragrance of your favourite flowers or herbs wafts under your nose. Imagine the smell of your favourite perfume, breathe slowly but deeply, and allow yourself to relax even more deeply.

Surprisingly, it's been more than six months since you smoked but you haven't missed it all. You have always wondered what it would like to be to stop smoking; you created this narrative in your head that it may not be as easy as it was, but now that you are experiencing it, you feel that you've never felt better in your life before.

You are only thinking about smoking now because I mentioned it, but the rest of the time it's a thing of the past, for you, it's a bad habit that you used to have.

Longer Pause

Six months have gone by, your health is regained, and you have more energy and self-respect. You feel cleaner, fresher, healthier, and fitter, as life is wonderful now for you. When you see someone else smoking you wonder how they could do that to themselves, putting that filthy thing into their mouth, inhaling the smoke, and the tar into their lungs. It seems pointless to you even though you know that sometime in the past you once did the same thing, but that was before you discovered a better way.

I want you to hold these good feelings right there, and tell yourself that, "I haven't smoked for six months, so why should I now". Now, remember the garden of perfume, the beauty of nature, and living in harmony with your mind, your body, and your spirit of love. Imagine holding on to those good feelings in your hand and clasping them in your fist if you like because the feelings are becoming so strong that you want to hold onto them forever.

Longer Pause

Now relax, as I'm bringing you back in time to (name the present date) and you're still feeling good. You clasp your hand again and tell yourself once more, "I haven't smoked for six months, so why should I now".

When you wake up from this hypnotic dream you will completely believe that you have not smoked for six months, and you will think to yourself that you don't want to smoke ever again. All other memories remain intact, but the fact is you truly feel as though you have not smoked for six whole months, why should you now. You will keep this belief to yourself because you know in your heart that you're a non-smoker and you hold that good feeling right there in your hand.

You could be anything you want to, so you are a non-smoker now. You've already been a non-smoker for six whole months, so it doesn't matter if you know that, on one hand, you had smoked in the past and on the other hand you have all those wonderful feelings that you gained in hypnosis from traveling six months into your beautiful future.

Longer Pause

When you wake up, you will have an inner belief that you have been a non-smoker for six months, so there's no point in starting again now. You're over it, smoking is a dead-end for you, you finished smoking before it finished you, and now you're free. You are completely in control of your habits.

Pause

What your subconscious mind can conceive, your conscious mind can achieve, like your belief that you've already stopped smoking grows stronger and stronger every day. Since you've already stopped smoking, there's no point in falling in the rabbit hole again.

Remain in hypnosis for another few minutes whilst you enjoy these wonderful feelings, just enjoy being here in your special place and notice how this place becomes a part of you. This is a wonderful place which you can visit again whenever you wish to, and all with the power of your mind.

Learning to Relax

Let's learn how to relax yourself every time you feel stressed.

You are now going to take in a deep breath, hold it for a few seconds and then exhale and try to relax.

Pause

Take in a second breath in your full capacity. And while you exhale, allow the stress persisting inside your mind to release. Allow it to let go.

Pause

For a third time, take in the third deep breath, try holding it as long as you can and as you exhale during that time, ask your mind to rest by saying "Relax now".

Consequently, always try to relax whenever you face a stressful situation. So whenever you feel stressed in the future just remember to follow the above steps, take three deep breaths, and at the end while you exhale quietly tell yourself the appellation "Relax now".

Longer Pause

You are now progressing towards developing a fresh way to relax. You are not concerned anymore about the stress of the past and now all you have decided is to relax and be peaceful. There is no space for stress in your life. Unhappiness, anger, irritation don't exist in your life. This not only hampers your physical health but disturbs emotional equilibrium which you don't want in your life.

From now on, follow a peaceful, calm life. It's the time to react in a controlled way in whatever you do because health is most precious.

Pause

Modifying your habits, changing the way of your action are your new habits now. These steps are for your wellbeing. I will give some more positive recommendations and by following it, you will experience that your life is stress-free and you will feel more relieved and relaxed in your daily routine.

The situations that stressed you in the past will no longer bother you. Moreover, this suggestion will make your lifestyle calm and composed, you will feel more cheerful. Appreciating your life is all that you need to think about from now.

Pause
The human mind is really complex. My first suggestion for you is that our mind may have

some dim view, negative mindset, lack of confidence, and you might be thinking that your future may be worse but now you are going to respond to this in a positive way by saying the word "Stop". I will tell you this again to make it more comprehensible. Each and every time you start having negative thoughts, gloomy outlook, you need to tell your mind to STOP.

Longer Pause

As soon as you command the word Stop, your bad thoughts will drop out of sight making your mind stress-free and it will let your mind welcome more clear, confident positive thoughts and will replace the negative thoughts making you believe in what's happening instead of what has happened.

Pause

From this day on, no matter whatever makes you stressed about any state of affairs which is not in your control or even if you imagine any uncertain situation, you will no longer get anxious about it and will accept whatever the situation brings to you. You will realize that accepting reality is a very important key.

Pause

Your mind is ready now to tackle any situation and you can now easily formulate the solution whatever the consequences are. You should act first before thinking about the result. Working out on your problems instead of worrying about it will let your mind free.

You are over and done with worrying, it is no more a part of your life. It is now replaced by a relaxing and peaceful mind.

Pause

At present, your thoughts, emotion, sentiment are in your control. You have control over them rather than they have over you.

We are noticing something very interesting, you have become an actor rather than a Re-actor. Let me elaborate on this, whenever you are in a stressful situation you are the one who is going to make the final decision on your actions in a particular situation. Now you choose to react calmly, with a positive attitude. You are completely under control.

Pause

Now just for a second, I would like to bring your attention to your breathing cycle. Start concentrating on your breathing, breathe in and breathe out, at the very moment when you start feeling that you have exhaled all the air, you can prepare yourself for another breathe count till 25 in silence, take a second breath now and it doesn't need to be a deep breath instead it can be a normal one.

Now start your breathing count up to 24. After that, take another breath for a duration that appears normal to you and then breathe out, counting up to 23 and continue counting from beginning to the end.

Longer Pause

At the very moment when you take your final deep breath just exhale out and count number one, you are now going to open your eyes. As you open your eyes you feel more insouciant, relaxed, and comfortable in all the senses. This feeling will make you refreshed more than ever.

Longer Pause

As I explain this to you, you continue counting each one of your breaths, focusing on the flow of your breathing and how it is filling your body and leaves. You will now feel every sensation. As you go more in-depth, you will start feeling more refreshed and relaxing. Once you open your eyes you will feel astonishing in every possible way.

Here begins your journey of quitting smoking. You are determined to give up smoking and this determination is going to lead you to success. And the road leading you to quit smoking will eventually relax your mind. Yes, you heard that right, you can now calm down and relax, now walk away from all this and make the most of it to feel serene and relaxed.

Pause

This is the time you have chosen for yourself so drop everything and walk away leaving all painful experiences behind and just be relaxed. Allow yourself to relax thoroughly, the more you will feel relaxed the more you will be progressing towards your goal of quitting smoking. You are here because of your strong and inclined determination to end this deadly habit of smoking.

And the reason for choosing this session is not due to the influence of others, you are here because of your absolute determination. You see today as a day which will make you a non-smoker for your whole life.

Longer Pause

Your life will not be in control of that small white piece of paper containing tobacco. You are the one who has taken full control over your urges for smoking. The first step has been already taken

here. You are now ready to transform into a non-smoker. You have to stick to your decision and at the end of this session, you will achieve the objective and come out of this session as a non-smoker.

Pause

Smoking will never be part of your future life, it will be eradicated once and forever and you will not smoke in any circumstances.

This obnoxious habit will be your past now.

This will be a brand-new rise of you and your current life as a non-smoker will never let you smoke again. So as the clock is ticking at the moment, imagine yourself as a non-smoker who has stopped smoking and the one who will by no means ever smoke again.

Currently, you are a non-smoker and have this ability to control your urge for smoking, even if you are surrounded by people who are smokers.

You know how to cherish your life even without smoking, you are aware of all pros and cons. Moreover, your life is happier and healthier now as a non-smoker.

As a fact of the matter, it makes no difference to you whether you are in the office, home, all alone, or with friends, your mind is in your control. Whether you are eating, driving, doing some tasks, or relaxing, solely that seems much more delightful as a non-smoker.

Pause

This feeling is phenomenal, your life is without any stress, and healthier. With each passing day, you will breathe without constraints.

Quitting this habit of smoking will not only be beneficial for your health but it will help you gain more confidence also.

Just make this confidence rush inside your spirit and mind, enable it to flow within you right now at this moment. You have to comprehend that you are a non-smoker with this confidence that you have attained, you need to live life.

It is not easy to quit such a habit, but you have conquered this journey very easily with your enthusiasm. At this moment you are filled with self-confidence and positiveness in your mind.

Longer Pause

It is essential to remember that to carry off anything worthwhile in your life you have to give your best shot. And it takes even more effort to continue to be a non-smoker that is 100% effort, 100% to succeed, and 100% to your dedication.

This commitment of yours is not made to anyone else but your true self and you are always going to give 100% to accomplish your target.

Presently you have stopped smoking, you became a non-smoker willingly and you will never smoke again in your life. As time passes your inclination, desire, promptness towards your health is strengthened with greater purpose.

Pause

Besides being a non-smoker, you have established a new positive habit, which is not only going to help you in the present but also for your entire life.

This moment forth, this feeling will be in a more striking manner than ever. You have exceeded in mastering this good habit of giving up on smoking. Instead of that, you have developed a habit of having water at proper duration which is beneficial for your health. This water will taste much more fresh and tonic. This refreshing water will fulfill your desire like it has never done before.

At the present moment, you must have started observing that whenever you think about the water you start feeling thirsty, there is no need to worry this is just your body's natural reflex.

Longer Pause

At this moment you are aware that you are not a smoker anymore, and filled with positive energy. This energy, liveliness will be used for other good deeds in your life. You are now realizing that you are feeling more positive by attending this session and it's guiding you through a happy life, you are experiencing intensified feelings about yourself. You have started utilizing your power in better habits like going to morning walk, you might be parking your car a little bit further so that you can walk for some more distance till you reach your office to do more physical work.

Adapting new healthy eating habits is your new hobby. These additional habits are instinctual by-products of becoming healthier. They are all the result of your true determination and will power.

Smoking Cessation II

As you are becoming more comfortable and relaxed, you will find your mind wandering here and there occasionally by drifting off in the direction it wants, but you know that it's okay. There is nothing big for you to do right now, there is no place to go, no problems to solve, nothing to do but to relax and let go, so relax your mind and let go of your worries.

Pause

As you let go, you become more aware of my voice, perhaps not consciously, but subconsciously you will listen to every word I say, and soon enough, my words will become your thoughts. Your thoughts will start to generate a whole new way of thinking, feeling, and will start being there for you.

Longer Pause

You have been having some unwanted troublesome thoughts for a while now and those thoughts preyed on your mind and made you feel like you are emotionally and physically ill. But count on changing the narrative, the changes will happen quite soon not because I say so and certainly not because of any miracle or even this hypnotic experience, but because you have decided to change. You have decided who you are, you took your control back and now, you alone are in charge of you.

Pause

It took a long time for experts like psychologists, doctors, and other people working in the field of neurological disorders to find that people don't have bad thoughts because they feel bad, but it is more often because it's the other way around. They constantly think that something wrong is going to happen which generates some uncomfortable emotions, and a feeling of general discomfort in them.

Considering everything, I have decided to show you the simplest technique in the world that will allow you to eliminate all those unwanted thoughts once and for all. You are going to use the 'thought stopping' technique together with your anchor to reinforce what you're learning which will double the effect of what you say to yourself to get rid of those thoughts.

Longer Pause

Let me explain the technique first and then we will go through some examples so we can strengthen your knowledge of how to apply it.

Whenever a bad thought comes into your mind I want you to *(if you are right-handed, then use it otherwise vice versa of the instruction)* use the middle three fingers of your right hand to gently slap over the middle three fingers of the left hand and say the word 'Stop'. When you say 'Stop', you are telling yourself that this thought is not true and you are not accepting the thought to be real.

To enable yourself to believe what you're saying, we will now go through one or two examples of typical negative thoughts.

Most people are misguided by their past mistakes and some toxic people around them. They think that they are bad people because they made a mistake or something went wrong in their life. You must have experienced such an occasion where you opened your mouth to say something and immediately regretted it after it came out of your mouth. You then go on to beat yourself up about it for ages afterward. Strangely enough, the more thought you give about that situation, the more power you are giving to it, it becomes stronger and you feel worse than you were feeling before.

Pause

If you took time to reflect and held that thought up to the light soon afterward and saw it for what it was, you would have realized that it was just a slip of the tongue or an inadvertent response. Does that make it your mistake? Does that make you a bad person? If someone else was in the same position, would you have punished them as much as you are punishing yourself? Exactly, I don't think so.

After a quick evaluation of this situation, you have decided that you're not bad after all; you slap yourself gently on the left hand and say the word 'Stop' to yourself. The exact words will be "Stop, this thought is not true and I am not accepting this thought to be real".

Pause

For instance, you are preparing for a test or perhaps awaiting the results of a medical examination, all sorts of things will go through your mind, like, "What if I fail?", "What if the result is negative?", "Is this the end of the world?". Hold those thoughts up to the light and see them clearly for what they are. If you fail an exam, it's not the end of the world; you can still prepare yourself better for another one. If it's a medical situation, your chances of recovery will be higher if you approach it with a positive mind, and the chance of your results being in your favor will be more than 50-50, so now slap yourself gently on the left hand and say the word 'Stop' to yourself. You will say, "Stop, this thought is not true and I am not accepting this thought to be real"

Longer Pause

You will learn to examine and evaluate your negative thoughts rapidly by slapping the thoughts out of your mind, you will realize that after just a short while that you can eliminate them instantly by using this six finger technique by saying the word 'Stop' to yourself.

You will say "Stop, this thought is not true and I am not accepting this thought to be real". It will go away if you follow this; it is as easy and as simple as that.

You are going to find yourself using this method more often to clean out those toxic thoughts, and the more you use these methods, the more strength you give to a positive outcome, soon you will realize that you are eliminating negative thoughts easily and rapidly because they are losing their power over you. They begin to diminish and you find yourself to be more positive with healthy thoughts which make you feel happier, calmer, and more confident than ever before.

These suggestions will be solidly embedded in your subconscious mind and will grow stronger day by day, they will grow firmer by the day and stronger by the hour and solid by the minute.

Hypnosis Benefits Script

A lot of people have been able to quit smoking under hypnosis. It is a heightened state of awareness that allows you to have easy access to what resides in your subconscious mind.

The hypnotic state is also called as trance and this is also called as the state of suspended disbelief. In this relaxed state of mind, you are able to let go of what your conscious mind thinks. In fact, the conscious takes a back seat and this also happens when you are reading an interesting book or looking outside the window for a longer period of time. Hypnosis is a pure relaxation and this audio only allows you to get into that state of mind.

And in this state of mind, you do not want a cigarette and you will continue to listen to the sound of my voice.

You get into the hypnotic state every now and then without consciously knowing it. And some of the everyday hypnosis examples are

You are in an elevator and as you continue to see the numbers go down, you know that you are going down and down knowing that each number down means each floor down…like

10, 9….8….7……6….5….4…

The door opens and you follow the people who are with you and move out of the elevator until you realize that you are on a wrong floor. And, you then wait for another elevator to come so that you can take that and reach the ground floor.

And, the other elevator comes and you step into it…and it starts to further go down and this time you are focused on the numbers and ….4….3...2….1….and 0.

Similarly, the experience of driving, when you are driving and you cross many traffic signals, crossroads, go through exits, thinking about something at work or listening to your favorite track and then you reach the destination without even realizing that it took you 30 minutes..

Or when you read an interesting book, you imagine the story in your mind and pay minimal attention to what is happening around you…because the conscious is aware of everything around you but does not interfere in you and your book. Because it takes a back seat.

And you have created the same state now…you are deeply relaxed where you are focused on the sound of my voice and your conscious mind has taken a back seat…and whatever is being said now goes directly into your subconscious mind…which is a powerhouse of knowledge and can help you change all the habits…which includes smoking too.

This is perhaps the light state or deep state of trance, it does not matter, because any state feels good. Isn't it?
A lot of people smoke as they believe that it helps them kill boredom, relax, and make them stress free. And, that is absolutely wrong. Smoking increases stress and impedes relaxation. And now you know of the trance state or hypnotic state…and how it can change any habit.

Longer Pause

You are good at inducing this state anytime and with self-hypnosis, you can direct your mind to change anything that serves no purpose.

In this state, you will be reprogramming your subconscious mind to set goals for better health. You will be letting go of a habit and making new choices as if you are cleaning an overflowing drawer of your end table.

And, I wonder if you could imagine cleaning the drawer that is full of clutter and how it is affecting your mood.

Pause

When you open the drawer, you notice old papers, filled diaries, pencils, non-working pens, wrappers of candies, some expired medicines, some accessories that are of no use….

Longer Pause

Take all of them out and put them in the trash can…and feel how you feel about the clean drawer…

Pause

As you notice the clean drawer, you notice you have now new space to put in things that are important for you…that do good to you…

Similarly, your subconscious is clean now to take in new information and the new information is that you are a non-smoker. And, you are motivated to stay a non-smoker.

Being a non-smoker makes you powerful, brave, and happier.

You take multivitamins including B complex and vitamin c regularly. You drink lots of water throughout the day to keep yourself hydrated. You pay more attention to your body and health. You love yourself even more now.

And it is so easy to stay as a non-smoker continuing to feel amazing about yourself and taking pride in it.

With every passing day, your will is becoming stronger and stronger as you are becoming even more relaxed and calmer.

Pause

You are a non-smoker and you enjoy being one.

You inspire others and tell them how you overcame it.

It is all about taking the decision, diverting the thoughts of cigarettes, consciously getting rid of the packs, and knowing that you need to live a fulfill your life.

You love your life and family immensely and you are an active non-smoker and a passive non-smoker.

Longer Pause

You stop yourself from standing and sitting with people who smoke.

And, if at all anyone offers you a cigarette, with high self-esteem and assertiveness, you know exactly what you need to say.

You straightforwardly say NO to them.

And, in no way you cannot make the same mistake which you perhaps made many times in the past because it is a waste of time and energy by quitting it for a few days and then going back to it.

You are very sure of your decision and you know it feels like to be a non-smoker and a smoker.

Silky Breathing

Continue to breathe and allow yourself to go deeper and deeper with every breath you take. And, I wonder if you can count your breath and as you do so and exhale…allow every little tension in your body go out…

As you continue to breathe, imagine, visualize, or feel your breath to be soft and smooth like silk. This feels like breathing in soft silk like breath…smooth and soft.

Pause

Perhaps you give it a color to the soft and silky breath…the most relaxing and calming color and as you imagine that, you allow that color to move into your face and head…that spreads down to the back of your head and neck, going further down to your spine, reaching upper back, middle, and lower back…

And imagine giving it a nice smell…a flower or your favorite perfume's fragrance. Whatever you like, give it a beautiful fragrance and imagine that fragrant silk moving down your hips, back of your thighs, calves, ankles, heels, and feet….

Pause

As you continue to breathe, you imagine the fragrant soft silk moving up into your shins, knees, thighs, torso, chest and shoulders…

Now, imagine it moving it into your lungs as you continue to feel the silk and smell its beautiful fragrance.

Longer Pause

And perhaps now the silk has a flavor too. And, the flavor that you like that enhances the experience…

Allow yourself to inhale the beautiful fragrance, color, and flavor of this silk and maybe now give it a sound…

Longer Pause

A sound that relaxes you…it could be a sound of the waves, your favorite tune, or anything that comes to your mind now. It could even me a vibration….

Pause

As you continue to breathe, you breathe in the sound, the fragrance, the flavor, the color, the feel…of the silk…

That's right.

It almost feels like a beautiful silk sheet all around you that feels so comfy and relaxing…and imagine this silky sheet becoming bigger and bigger and covering you from all sides…

Pause

You feel so comfy having it around you…you feel safe and comfortable. It wraps you and soothes every emotion and thought.
This is now your sheet of comfort and you can imagine it having on and around you every time you feel stressed in future.

Pause

It relaxes your feelings and thoughts as it carries the calming sound, your favorite fragrance, the relaxing color, the silky touch, and the flavor wrapping you from all sides…

And all thoughts regarding cigarettes simply melt away…would you like the thought of smoke and the smell of smoke to remain in this silky sheet?

I know your answer is No…and perhaps it would be the same for me…

All the thoughts about smoking leave your silky sheet and go far away from you…

Pause

Imagine going further deep into this comforting state of relaxation and allow your subconscious mind to open to the suggestions

And repeat in your mind after me…

I love being healthy (4-5 seconds pause)

I have taken charge of my health (4-5 seconds pause)

I love myself and my body fully (4-5 seconds pause)

Pause

Now imagine that the corner of the silky sheet is between your fingers and palm and you tighten your fist to feel it better…

And as you do so, you feel the softness and silkiness between the fingers and palm…

This is a reminder that every time you need to feel calm and relaxed, you simply have to tighten your fist and you will enter this same state of relaxation

Especially, when you crave a cigarette, all you have to do is only tighten your fist and the thoughts about it will leave you and go far away…

Pause

I wonder if you can now imagine a tall clear glass of water. It is cool and clean…

Imagine having a sip and feel the water go down your throat, reaching the chest, and your stomach…

Having more water has many benefits as it flushes out the toxins, helps in losing weight, gives more mental clarity, keeps you alert…and makes you productive.

You can enjoy the benefits of water by having at least 8 glasses of cool and clean water everyday…

Longer Pause

Perhaps it also cleanses you of the thoughts about the cigarettes.

Imagine having a tall glass of water now and notice how instantly you feel relaxed, calm, and positive…

Every time you take a sip, you feel stronger about staying non-smoker.

This only means, that water replaces cigarettes.

Pause

The more water you consume, the stronger you feel about staying a non-smoker.

That's right.

Now, let's come back to the silky breathing…imagine breathing in your favorite fragrance, the calming color, the melodious sound, the soft touch, and your favorite flavor…

Pause

Imagine the silky sheet all around you. You feel so calm and relaxed…that you want to just sleep and drift further into an even better state of relaxation.

Staying Committed Script

Notice how your breathing is, soft and fragrant...like silk.

And as you continue to listen to me and enjoy this beautiful state of relaxation, I wonder if you can imagine yourself in a beautiful open meadow.

The grass in lush green and moist...and imagine it beneath your feet. Feel it underneath and look around. The surroundings are beautiful, the weather is perfect, it is breezy, and the sunshine is warm and crisp.

Longer Pause

You can feel the breeze against your skin and as you feel that, you notice tall trees in front of you that are swaying with the wind...and this meadow is a place to learn.

In the front, you notice a beautiful white path with dry leaves on it. You decide to walk on it and as you move forward, you notice hearing your own footsteps...

And moving forward means moving towards your future...

What's behind is the past...your past where you experienced a lot as a child or a teenager or an adult...learnt many lessons.

And in front, you have a life that you have not experienced really but where you are right now, with all the decisions you have made, you know you will be able to make your future better...and decide on better things..

Isn't it...

Longer Pause

You keep walking and reach a place where the path splits into two. One path goes to the left and the other path goes to the right...you are the fork in the path.

Allow your mind to rest here.

You have a choice to make now...each path has its own possibilities...

The left path is almost like the path as your past...with same lifestyle, same life, same habits...

The right path has new possibilities with better health, a new and healthier lifestyle, stronger and clear mind, better sleep, and much more...

You are at the deciding point and as you stand at the fork, you know that you have to make a commitment to being a non-smoker. To stay as a non-smoker for the rest of your life. You want to be healthier and happier...living a fulfilling life and having a longer life.

This is a decision for life. So, you decide to walk both paths before you take that decision.

Longer Pause

You step on the path to your left...and start to walk on it...and the life here is pretty much the same. You are smoking, coughing, having breathing issues. You have the feelings of guilt about smoking, you want to quit but unable to. You are struggling to quit, you feel stressed, and tired.

Many years down the line, you see yourself as getting older before time, it seems the cigarettes have taken a toll on your skin. You are getting wrinkles before time, the skin looks dehydrated, you cough most of the times, and your body feels fatigued.

The family members love you a lot, however, they feel disappointed in you. They wish if you could quit smoking and live joyously with them for a long time.

You know that the life will remain the same on this path...the path of constant struggle, guilt, and disappointment.

Now, imagine going back to the fork.

Pause

You are back at the fork in the path...and because you need to make the decision today about commitment, you decide to walk the path to your right...to see how the future will be if you chose this path.

Take the right path now...

And as you step on it, you feel the cool breeze against your face...the air here is clean. You are breathing in fresh and clean air...few steps down the path, you notice living a healthier life...

Everything here is positive and you feel confident and calm. There is a sense of freedom and lightness...you are energetic, active, and healthy.

The friends and family here admire you and get inspired by the choices you have made. Further down the path, you notice yourself living an amazing life with your family and friends. Life is really good here.

You have a clearer mind and a fitter body. The older you get, the healthier you get, your skin looks young and feel energetic, positive, and much happier.

This life lifts you up in every way...

Longer Pause

Now come back to the fork.

Pause

And as you stand at the fork, you now know how each path looks in the future and you now have to make a choice and decide on the path that will make you happier, positive, and healthier. So, whether you want to live a free, healthy and happy life or live a tiring, unhealthy, and mediocre life, is your choice.

Look at the paths again as you stand at the fork. And as you stand here, you reach your inner wisdom and get guidance.

Longer Pause

What is it that you want to do?

Allow your mind to prepare and imagine that there is a panel in your brain that takes care of urges, desires, cravings, habits, thoughts, and emotions...

Reach that place in your mind NOW.

Notice the panel and it has many switches and pulleys. I wonder if you find a switch for cigarettes. If yes, switch it off immediately.

That's right..

And, now that it is switched off, you know that the thoughts pertaining to cigarettes wont enter your mind. And you will never have to worry about stopping the cravings or diverting your mind. The cigarette switch is completely OFF.

And, now that it is turned off, it's going to be easier and effortless to choose the right path.

The path to your right is the right path…isn't it?

Step on it now.

Pause

And as you step on the path of healthier life, you feel proud of yourself to have taken this decision. Life feels amazing her. The world here looks so much better. You are free, happier, positive, and healthier. You breathe clean and fresh air, your lungs are perfect, your skin glows, you look much younger than your age.

You are a non-smoker.

As you continue to walk on the path, you notice that after few years, you have become emotionally and mentally stronger. The health has improved manifold. The decision of quitting smoking has added many years to your life.

The life here is amazing. You have better relationships with people. People love you for your strong will power. You have been inspiring them.

You are so grateful that you made the decision long ago and are sticking to it. You are committed to being a non-smoker.

You are a non-smoker

It is so easy to stay as a non-smoker

And it is very important for you to stay as a non-smoker.

You are happy being a non-smoker because the results are phenomenal. You love yourself fully and completely. You love your body, your health, your life, and the decision you made.

These suggestions will go deeper into your subconscious mind…with every passing moment…

That's right.

Get rid of the Compulsion Script

As you continue to listen to me and take each breath, you are drifting further down in a deeper state of mind that allows you to be more attentive to what I am saying.

As you relax, you feel so proud and confident about making this positive change in your life. The change that will give you great health and allow you to live a fulfilling life.

Every word I say causes you to embrace health and reject smoking or cigarettes. Every time you listen to this audio, it reinforces the fact that you are a non-smoker 1000 times. You are free from the old nasty and smelly habit of yours. Every part of your being enjoys being free and breathing in clean and fresh air.

Pause

Your organs are thanking you for making this important decision.

You are in control of your choices and you are celebrating this freedom and are proud of the decision you have made.

The part of you perhaps thought of smoking and the other part is this who is listening to me, who wants to live as a non-smoker.

Pause

And you have already spoken to that part that he will be your friend to keep you stay focused on the life time goal of staying a non-smoker always. You are not going to be the slaves of the old habit and it feels amazing to be in control and free.

You are in charge of your choices, decisions, and behaviours. You have decided to choose a life that is healthier giving you better health, longer life, clear throat, better skin, and fresher breath. And there is no stench of tobacco in your hands and hair.

With no smoke smell in your hands, hair, and clothes, you appear much more attractive to your friends, family, and your partner.

Pause

You also notice your teeth getting cleaner and gums becoming healthier. You are totally free of tobacco and this leads to a happy and healthier life. You are a non smoker for the rest of your life. No amount of tension or stress can let you pick up smoking. You have better ways to cope up with stress or tension that does not harm your body.

You had come to a fork in the path and you saw yourself living a healthy life and decided on living a healthy smoke free life. You also saw how the path with smoking looked and felt like.

Pause

And every part of you, have together decided on take the path of non-smoking. The road you have already taken is the road of tobacco free life.

Anytime, there is a faintest thought about cigarette in your mind, you simply reject it. You get reminded of the path you have chosen and you reinforce the fact in your mind that you have chosen this path, you take responsibility of it. And this gives you immense confidence and the feeling of significance that you have been able to bring positive changes to your life.

Pause

If you happen to be around smokers, you feel as if you have never smoked and the smell in the air causes your mind to reject smoking, which is 1000 times more powerful. There is a sense of pride you feel every time you reject a cigarette or reject a thought about it. The self-respect increases and you feel courage and strength in yourself.

You also think about how much money have you wasted in the past on cigarettes. And, how much you can save now with this decision. Perhaps, use that money to enjoy better things in life. Maybe a vacation, gym membership, learning courses, so on and so forth.

And, because you have chosen to be a non-smoker, you have created a new truth for you. This truth is planted in the deepest part of your being and guides your new life as a non-smoker.

Longer Pause

The truth is that you are a non-smoker. And, you keep hearing this in your mind every now and then. This may have many variations but the meaning would be same. You may hear statements like – I love to be a non-smoker, I am a non-smoker for life, I choose to be a non-smoker, I reject smoking. I think and feel like a non-smoker.

Your subconscious mind locks this new truth deep into the deepest part of you so that it becomes your reality and you live this truth in the real world.

Pause

The second new truth is: I have NO desire to smoke. I reject smoking subconsciously and consciously.

And this again goes deeper into your deepest part of your mind and becomes your reality.

The next truth is that Smoking is a thing of past. You have released all the smoking and all of that stays in the past as if it has been locked in the past. There is no way that it can come forward and be a part of your current life. Smoking is a thing of past. Your past holds all the effects of smoking. In this current time, you are a non-smoker.

Pause

The truth is: I have moved past my past. Smoking is a thing of past.

And, the next truth is again – I am a non-smoker. I am permanently free from smoking. And, this goes further deep into your subconscious mind. This makes you feel empowered, confident, and wise.

Pause

In this place of new truths, you are a non-smoker, you have a zero desire to smoke, smoking is a thing of past, and you are a non-smoker. You are free from smoking. You enjoy this freedom as a non-smoker. You love your health and love your body.

And these new truths lock themselves in your subconscious mind. You hear them always at the back of your mind, like a background music. Every time you hear each truth, you are all the more determined to stay focused on the journey of being a non smoker. These truths are unbreakable and unshakeable. This is your new reality and you choose to stay as a non-smoker for the rest of your life. Living healthily and happily.

And as I count down from 5 down to 1, these suggestions will go deeper into your subconscious mind.

Pause

Starting now at 5, going deeper at 4….further deep at 3….locking themselves in the deepest part of your subconscious mind….2……locked….1…..you are a non smoker..

Live a Smoke Free Life

And you continue to drift deeper and deeper into this relaxed state of mind and as you continue to drift, you begin to relax even more and enjoy the wonderful feeling of being at calm. And, everything is perfect right now.

Pause

All the stress and tensions have gone far away leaving you here feeling absolutely peaceful and relaxed. You are going with the flow as you continue to listen to each word I say. No one wants anything from you…and this makes you so much more relaxed that you can fully focus in here and now.

And, I want to say a big congratulations to you for making this wonderful decision to quit smoking and living your life in a healthier way. With the commitment you have made, you have shown yourself that you can do take great decisions in life for your health and live healthily.

Pause

We are going to use the same positive reinforcement now in this state of your mind so that it goes deeper into your subconscious mind and you continue to stay committed to yourself and continue to stay non-smoker for the rest of your life.

You are listening to me because you want to stay a non-smoker for the rest of your life and because you have already seen the effects of smoking. And it can have serious repercussions on your health later in life. And, because of this, you have already quit it and feel so proud of taking that decision.

Pause

From today on you look forward to having an amazing life where you give your health utmost priority. You see yourself in future as a healthy person enjoying all the good things in life. You have overcome an old habit of yours that did not do any good to you. And this only reinforces that you will continue to keep yourself healthy without any nicotine in your body.

And with every passing day, your old way of life fades away into a distant memory…as if you come out of a tunnel and is all brightness and sunshine all around you.

Pause

You are always conscious of the motivation and determination to stay healthy and keep your body clean, which ultimately makes you active, energetic, and happy.

You put good things in your mouth, things that give you nutrition and makes you go on without causing any bad effects to your body. And all these things include good food, lots of water, and healthy drinks. You eat healthy and you breathe in healthy air. And all of this is visible on your body and face in no time.

Perhaps you have already started to see the difference on your face and body. Perhaps your face has gotten clearer…

Longer Pause

You are very happy with the decision that you have made to live a healthier and happier life. This also include the feelings of pride and courage. You have been courageous to take that decision and stick to it and that gives you the feeling of pride. And these feelings grow deeper and deeper with every passing day and with every word I say.

You are aware that your actions have a direct influence on the friends and family. And the decision of quitting smoking is setting a great example for the people so that they also know that if you can do it then anyone can do it. And everyone looks upto you and talk about you to others. This way you are not only helping the people you know directly but also the people you do not know like the friends of your friends and family.

Pause

And when you think about your old life. You think that you were stupid to have smoked for so long and life seems so much better without cigarettes. You again feel relieved by knowing that you have taken a right decision to be happier, healthier, more active and inspiring.

Pause

You are free from all the unwanted habits and addiction and you are proud of it. You have a strong will power and your mind is committed to the decision and continue to stay committed because you love yourself a lot and in no way you can let damage yourself.

Affirmations

1. You are a non-smoker (7 seconds pause)
2. You breathe better (7 seconds pause)
3. You love your body and you take utmost care of it (7 seconds pause)
4. You look forward to living a smoke free life (7 seconds pause)
5. You hate cigarettes (7 seconds pause)
6. Cigarettes remind you of cancer and all the costs that come with it (7 seconds pause)
7. You enjoy being a non-smoker (7 seconds pause)
8. You love yourself unconditionally (7 seconds pause)
9. You save money as a non-smoker (7 seconds pause)
10. You love yourself (7 seconds pause)
11. You love your body (7 seconds pause)
12. You want to live a long life (7 seconds pause)
13. You want to enjoy the gifts of life (7 seconds pause)
14. You drink 8 to 10 glasses of water everyday (7 seconds pause)
15. You take care of your health everyday (7 seconds pause)
16. You love to exercise (7 seconds pause)
17. You sleep on time and take care of your sleep cycle (7 seconds pause)

18. Your skin improves with every passing day as a non-smoker (7 seconds pause)
19. Your skin glows with health and radiance (7 seconds pause)
20. You breathe fresh air (7 seconds pause)
21. You have more interesting things to do as a non-smoker (7 seconds pause)
22. You love being a non-smoker (7 seconds pause) (7 seconds pause)
23. You feel amazing as a non-smoker (7 seconds pause)
24. Your self love and self-appreciation has increased (7 seconds pause)
25. You respect your body, mind, and soul (7 seconds pause)
26. Everyday, you are feeling healthier and happier (7 seconds pause)
27. You prefer to breathe fresh air every day (7 seconds pause)
28. You choose to live as a non smoker (7 seconds pause)
29. You choose to not smoke and feel great about yourself (7 seconds pause)
30. You live a smoke free life (7 seconds pause)
31. Your lungs are feeling great with every passing day (7 seconds pause)
32. You love your freedom as a non-smoker (7 seconds pause)
33. You have a deep love for your body (7 seconds pause)
34. Your self-esteem improves as a non-smoker (7 seconds pause)
35. Your breathing has improved tremendously (7 seconds pause)

36. You are able to taste food better (7 seconds pause)
37. You are much calmer and relaxed as a non-smoker (7 seconds pause)
38. You are so happy to have given up smoking completely (7 seconds pause)
39. Your sleep cycle is getting better (7 seconds pause)
40. You sleep better and fall asleep faster (7 seconds pause)
41. You have taken charge of your health and body and that makes you feel amazing (7 seconds pause)
42. You are so happy as a non-smoker (7 seconds pause)
43. You are proud of yourself to have overcome nicotine addiction (7 seconds pause)
44. You are stronger than a cigarette (7 seconds pause)
45. You are the master of your mind (7 seconds pause)
46. You have control on your thoughts (7 seconds pause)
47. You are proud to have a healthy lifestyle (7 seconds pause)
48. You inspire people (7 seconds pause)
49. You breathe better (7 seconds pause)
50. You breathe fresh air (7 seconds pause)
51. You are stronger than any habit (7 seconds pause)
52. You can change habits easily (7 seconds pause)
53. You choose to live a healthy and happy life (7 seconds pause)

54. You overcome unhealthy habits easily (7 seconds pause)
55. You deserve an amazing life (7 seconds pause)
56. You are incredible and powerful (7 seconds pause)
57. You are positive and happier (7 seconds pause)
58. From now on, you are a permanent non-smoker (7 seconds pause)
59. Smoking is a thing of past (7 seconds pause)
60. You relax yourself easily when you are stressed (7 seconds pause)
61. You manage stress easily (7 seconds pause)
62. You don't let anything affect your life (7 seconds pause)
63. You are living a smoke free life (7 seconds pause)
64. Life is all good and healthy now (7 seconds pause)
65. You love yourself a lot (7 seconds pause)
66. Life is beautiful (7 seconds pause)
67. You love your body (7 seconds pause)
68. Your health is most important for you (7 seconds pause)
69. You breathe fresh and clean air (7 seconds pause)
70. Your lungs are getting healed (7 seconds pause)
71. Your body is your sacred place (7 seconds pause)
72. You love yourself (7 seconds pause)

73. You are full of vitality and energy (7 seconds pause)
74. You love to exercise because it makes you happy (7 seconds pause)
75. You are releasing weight effortlessly (7 seconds pause)
76. You are willing to change (7 seconds pause)
77. You let go of the past easily (7 seconds pause)
78. You are getting energetic with every passing day (7 seconds pause)
79. You pay attention to your sleep (7 seconds pause)
80. I am strong and healthy. (7 seconds pause)
81. You drink at least eight glasses of water everyday (7 seconds pause)
82. You look forward to your daily workout sessions. (7 seconds pause)
83. You listen to the signal and stop when you have eaten enough (7 seconds pause)
84. You are healthy and happy (7 seconds pause)
85. You love to exercise everyday (7 seconds pause)
86. You love to eat fruits and vegetables everyday (7 seconds pause)
87. You are becoming stronger and slimmer with every passing day (7 seconds pause)

88. When you crave sugar, you eat natural foods (7 seconds pause)
89. You are grateful for your health (7 seconds pause)
90. You are practice gratitude everyday (7 seconds pause)
91. You are open to new ways of eating (7 seconds pause)
92. You choose food that make your body stronger and healthier (7 seconds pause)
93. You chew food slowly (7 seconds pause)
94. You relish each mouthful and chew food at least 10 times (7 seconds pause)
95. You are becoming slimmer and lighter every day (7 seconds pause)
96. You love your body and mind (7 seconds pause)
97. You enjoy taking care of your body and mind (7 seconds pause)
98. You maintain sleep hygiene everyday (7 seconds pause)
99. You limit your day time naps to 30 minutes (7 seconds pause)
100. You can do it (7 seconds pause)
101. You are flexible (7 seconds pause)
102. You listen to your body (7 seconds pause)
103. You eat in moderation (7 seconds pause)

104. You eat wholesome foods (7 seconds pause)
105. You leave your past behind (7 seconds pause)
106. You feel decisive and enthusiastic (7 seconds pause)
107. You love your life (7 seconds pause)
108. You set everyday sleep and weight loss goals (7 seconds pause)
109. You take everyday actions to achieve goals (7 seconds pause)
110. You are motivated (7 seconds pause)
111. You focus on the good (7 seconds pause)
112. You are grateful (7 seconds pause)
113. You are happy (7 seconds pause)
114. You are self-aware (7 seconds pause)
115. pause)
116. .You see beauty in your body (7 seconds pause)
117. You learn new ways easily (7 seconds pause)
118. Your body is getting healed (7 seconds pause)
119. Every day you wake up you have feelings of gratitude (7 seconds pause)
120. You trust the process of life (7 seconds pause)
121. You trust yourself and trust your body (7 seconds pause)
122. You love yourself (7 seconds pause)
123. You are compassionate towards yourself (7 seconds pause)

124. You eat mindfully and enjoy every mouthful (7 seconds pause)
125. You are balanced (7 seconds pause)
126. You are competent and capable. (7 seconds pause)
127. You are worthy of love and care (7 seconds pause)
128. You give all the love and care to your own body first (7 seconds pause)
129. You choose positive thoughts (7 seconds pause)
130. You are blessed and abundant (7 seconds pause)
131. You love yourself unconditionally (7 seconds pause)
132. You are complete and whole. (7 seconds pause)
133. You are confident and courageous (7 seconds pause)
134. You forgive yourself for all the past mistakes (7 seconds pause)
135. You stay in present and are more mindful (7 seconds pause)
136. You are confident (7 seconds pause)
137. You have high self-esteem (7 seconds pause)
138. You are losing weight every day (7 seconds pause)
139. You are focused on your weight loss journey (7 seconds pause)
140. You pay attention to your food intake (7 seconds pause)

141. You love yourself unconditionally (7 seconds pause)
142. You are successful (7 seconds pause)
143. You are confident and motivated (7 seconds pause)
144. You believe in yourself (7 seconds pause)
145. You are good enough (7 seconds pause)
146. You enjoy healthy foods (7 seconds pause)
147. You do pleasurable activities everyday (7 seconds pause)
148. You are intelligent and wise (7 seconds pause)
149. You are lovable, open to receive and give love (7 seconds pause)
150. You enjoy your life (7 seconds pause)
151. You enjoy healthy food (7 seconds pause)
152. You have a beautiful relationship with food and your body (7 seconds pause)
153. You enjoy sleep and able to relax yourself easily (7 seconds pause)
154. You enjoy the process of self-hypnosis (7 seconds pause)
155. You enjoy being successful (7 seconds pause)
156. You inspire people by overcoming smoking (7 seconds pause)
157. You enjoy the benefits of being a non-smoker (7 seconds pause)

158. You imagine living a wonderful and long life as a non -smoker (7 seconds pause)
159. You spend more time with your family (7 seconds pause)
160. You let go of all the unhealthy habits (7 seconds pause)
161. You are success (7 seconds pause)
162. You are love (7 seconds pause)
163. You are happy (7 seconds pause)
164. You are positive (7 seconds pause)
165. You have high self-worth (7 seconds pause)
166. You enjoy living a quality life (7 seconds pause)
167. Life is wonderful (7 seconds pause)
168. You enjoy each day and live it to the fullest (7 seconds pause)
169. You are productive (7 seconds pause)
170. You enjoy being a non smoker (7 seconds pause)
171. You are a non smoker (7 seconds pause)
172. You are living a smoke free life (7 seconds pause)
173. You hate the thought of smoking and cigarettes (7 seconds pause)
174. You enjoy every day (7 seconds pause)
175. You are a healthy non smoker (7 seconds pause)
176. You are healthy and enjoy being healthy (7 seconds pause)

177. You keep your health on priority (7 seconds pause)
178. You enjoy all the benefits you see as a non smoker(7 seconds pause)
179. You are loved (7 seconds pause) (7 seconds pause)
180. You are open to give and receive love (7 seconds pause)
181. You are in control (7 seconds pause)
182. You have high control on your habits and thoughts (7 seconds pause)
183. Your health is getting better with every passing day (7 seconds pause)
184. Your body is healing (7 seconds pause)
185. Your body is getting repaired from the smoke (7 seconds pause)
186. You lungs are healing (7 seconds pause)
187. You protect your inner child always (7 seconds pause)
188. You are whole and complete (7 seconds pause)
189. You love yourself unconditionally (7 seconds pause)
190. You are a non-smoker (7 seconds pause)
191. You take care of your health always (7 seconds pause)
192. You exercise regularly (7 seconds pause)
193. You eat healthy foods (7 seconds pause)

194. You enjoy the tastes of healthy foods (7 seconds pause)
195. Your sense of taste and smell is getting better with every passing day (7 seconds pause)
196. You listen to this recording regularly (7 seconds pause)
197. You are a healthy non-smoker (7 seconds pause)
198. You are assertive (7 seconds pause)
199. You easily say NO to cigarettes (7 seconds pause)
200. You are an example for smoking cessation (7 seconds pause)